# Freezing and Thawing
## of Concrete—
# Mechanisms and Control

AMERICAN CONCRETE INSTITUTE MONOGRAPH SERIES

# Freezing and Thawing
# of Concrete—
# Mechanisms and Control

## WILLIAM A. CORDON

PUBLISHED JOINTLY BY

AMERICAN CONCRETE INSTITUTE
DETROIT, MICHIGAN
THE IOWA STATE UNIVERSITY PRESS
AMES, IOWA

# ACI Monograph No. 3

This monograph is published in furtherance of ACI objectives in the fields of engineering education and technology. The Institute is not responsible, as a body, for the statements and opinions advanced in this publication; Institute authority attaches only to standards adopted as provided in the ACI By-laws.

Copyright © 1966 American Concrete Institute
P.O. Box 4754, Redford Station
Detroit, Michigan 48219
Manufactured in the United States of America
Stock # 0705

Second printing, 1967

Library of Congress Catalog Card Number: 66–14390

**Also in this series:**

Lessons from Failures of Concrete Structures, by Jacob Feld—ACI Monograph No. 1

Evaluation of Concrete Properties from Sonic Tests, by E. A. Whitehurst—ACI Monograph No. 2

# Foreword

THE THIRD BOOK IN THE ACI Monograph Series has been prepared by a widely known consultant in the field of concrete and concrete materials, a man with more than a quarter of a century of research and testing experience. This work has been selected by ACI Committee 103, Monographs, with the hope that it will contribute to prevention of freezing and thawing damage to concrete.

Since its founding in 1905, one well-defined objective of the American Concrete Institute has been the gathering and dissemination of information about the properties and uses of plain and reinforced concrete and their constituent materials. ACI Committee 103 was organized to implement this purpose through publication of monographs dealing with specialized areas of subject matter within the broad field of concrete.

The committee, which began as a task group of the Technical Activities Committee in 1960, was officially designated Committee 103 in 1963. It is the Committee's plan that monograph manuscripts will be prepared by highly qualified authorities in the several fields to be treated. Technical content of all monographs will reflect the thinking and experience of the writers, and not necessarily that of Committee 103.

It is intended that each monograph in the series will develop a thorough understanding of the subject, and will summarize and evaluate the basic elements of existing knowledge and opinion on that topic. Free from the space limitations necessary for an ACI JOURNAL paper, the monograph writers will be able to provide a more thorough and complete treatment of their subject.

These monographs are tailored neither for the uninformed layman nor for the well-informed few. Rather it is intended that these publications be of maximum value to the practicing engineer, contractor, advanced student, and others having knowledge of concrete and its properties.

ACI COMMITTEE 103

# Contents

# ABOUT THE AUTHOR

WILLIAM A. CORDON, A WIDELY KNOWN CONSULTANT in the field of concrete and concrete materials, is associate professor of civil engineering at Utah State University, Logan. A native of Rigby, Idaho, he received his BS and MS degrees from Utah State University, and has done graduate work at Purdue University, the University of Minnesota, and the University of Colorado. The early years of Professor Cordon's career were spent in dam construction with the U. S. Bureau of Reclamation. He served as construction inspector at Grand Coulee Dam, Washington, earthwork inspector at Grassy Lake Dam in Wyoming, and was chief inspector and head of the field laboratory for Island Park Dam in Idaho.

From 1941 to 1954, Professor Cordon was assigned to the research laboratories of the Bureau of Reclamation at Denver, where he became head of the concrete and concrete materials section of the research and geology division. During this time he suggested an improved method for drainage of concrete dams, which brought him an award for excellence from the Secretary of the Interior.

In 1954 Professor Cordon joined the Portland Cement Association staff as research engineer, and in 1956 went to Utah State University where he has been engaged in both teaching and research. He is now in charge of the University's structural materials research laboratory.

Professor Cordon joined the American Concrete Institute in 1937 and has maintained a continuing high level of participation in affairs of the Institute. He is presently a member of the ACI Technical Activities Committee and chairman of ACI Committees 115, Research, and 533, Precast Wall Panels. He is also a member of ACI Committees 116, 201, 211, and 214, and past chairman of Committee 116, Proportioning of Concrete Mixes. He headed ACI Committee 214 when that committee developed ACI Standard 214-57, a method of evaluating strength tests of field concrete.

A member of Sigma Xi and Sigma Tau, Professor Cordon received the ACI Wason Medal with L. H. Tuthill in 1957 for their paper, "Properties and Uses of Initially Retarded Concrete." This was only one of his numerous technical papers which have been published by ACI, ASTM, and the Highway Research Board, as well as in technical periodicals abroad. Professor Cordon has also developed several new tests and testing apparatus for concrete.

# Freezing and Thawing of Concrete—
# Mechanisms and Control

# 1

# Introduction

PORTLAND CEMENT CONCRETE IS COMPOSED of some of the most abundant and durable materials in the earth's crust. Portland cement is manufactured essentially from silica and calcium, two of the most common minerals. Natural concrete aggregates are generally stable rock minerals which have withstood the forces of erosion and disintegration. Crushed aggregates from the parent rock of the earth's crust are also generally stable and durable. Notable exceptions are aggregates containing amorphorus silica in an unstable form which reacts with alkalies in portland cement. Reaction between portland cement and certain impure carbonate rocks has also recently been noted.

The durability of concrete and its ability to withstand the disruptive forces of nature has resulted in its reputation for permanence. A number of structures in existence have performed satisfactorily for hundreds of years. Portions of concrete structures built by the Romans are still standing after 2000 years. Although this concrete was not made with modern portland cement, it does illustrate the stability and permanence of concrete materials.

In spite of the basic durability of concrete, a number of concrete structures have not exhibited characteristics of permanence. Signs of deterioration and distress are sometimes apparent after a few months of service. Studies have demonstrated that concrete is susceptible to freezing and thawing action when moisture is present. Deterioration also occurs due to the reaction between certain reactive aggregates and the alkalies in portland cement. Soluble sulfates, in either the soil or water in which the concrete structure is placed, also attack concrete. This monograph is limited, however, to the effects of freezing and thawing on portland cement concrete.

Before 1900, most of the work on the behavior of concrete exposed to freezing and thawing was primarily concerned with the degradation of building stone and concrete aggregates and the behavior of concrete placed in freezing weather. Apparently the effect of the repetition of freezing and thawing cycles was not considered until after the turn of the century.

In the late 1920's and early 1930's there was considerable research in the field of concrete durability. These researches resulted in recommendations for producing durable concrete published in the Joint Committee Report on concrete and reinforced concrete, June 1940.[1]* Maximum water-cement ratios were established for different types of construction and exposure conditions. These recommendations are found in many publications and are still accepted as criteria for producing durable concrete.

The discovery of the beneficial effects of air entrainment in concrete was a cooperative effort by many organizations. One of the first articles on the subject was by Swayze (1941).[2] Although this paper reported that additions to cement of organic materials such as mineral oils, animal or vegetable fats, or natural resins result in concrete of greater durability, improved workability, and reduced bleeding, it did not mention entrained air. Some reduction in strength occurred, but the resistance to freezing and thawing was substantially increased. Extensive research by many interested organizations provided conclusive proof that it was indeed air entrainment

---

* All references cited by number appear at the end of the text on page 82. In addition, there is a selected bibliography of significant publications dealing with freezing and thawing deterioration, beginning on p. 88. These bibliography entries are not specifically cited in the text.

in concrete which provided protection against freezing and thawing. Symposiums on the subject of concrete containing air-entraining agents were presented by the American Concrete Institute in 1944 and 1946.[3,4]

Since the discovery of air entrainment and its influence on the behavior of concrete exposed to freezing and thawing, extensive research has been conducted covering the ramifications of the influence of entrained air in concrete. There is no longer doubt that concrete can be produced which will adequately resist certain types of freezing and thawing deterioration by using air entrainment, with high quality paste and durable aggregates.

It is the purpose of this monograph to discuss the behavior of various concrete structures exposed to freezing and thawing, to present theories regarding mechanisms which cause this behavior, and to describe methods of overcoming the mechanisms and preventing concrete deterioration.

# 2

# Deterioration of Concrete
# Exposed to Freezing
# and Thawing

THERE IS LITTLE DOUBT THAT DETERIORATION in concrete
structures due to freezing and thawing is one of the major
problems of the concrete industry in northern climates. This
undoubtedly raises a question in the mind of the public regarding the permanence and usefulness of concrete as a construction material.

The deterioration of concrete structures due to freezing
and thawing is usually conspicuous and easily recognized.
Scaling and spalling of pavements produces uneven, unsightly
surfaces even though the pavement may otherwise be sound
and of adequate quality. Freezing and thawing may ultimately
damage concrete structures seriously. On the other hand,
crumbling of cement paste and exposure of concrete aggregates in conspicuous locations give the impression that the
structure is on the verge of disintegration, even though the
deterioration due to freezing and thawing has not significantly
affected the structural stability and usefulness of the structure.
Extensive cracking and popouts also produce unsightly concrete surfaces.

## D-LINE CRACKING

One common indication of freezing and thawing deterioration is the appearance of cracks which run approximately parallel to joints or edges of concrete surfaces. As deterioration progresses these parallel cracks occur farther away from the joint. This type of cracking has been designated as D-line (deterioration line) cracking.

Typical examples of progressive D-line cracking are shown in Figure 2.1. Deterioration started at the sidewalk

Figure 2.1A—Typical D-line cracking beginning to develop along a sidewalk joint (photograph retouched to emphasize direction of cracking).


Figure 2.1B—D-line cracking spreading from sidewalk joint, and disintegration starting.

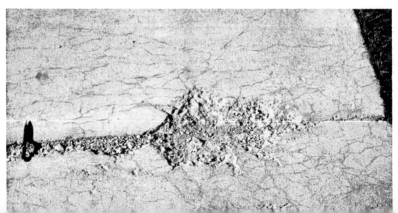

Figure 2.1C—Advanced stages of deterioration with D-line cracking developing along a structural crack.

joint and D-line cracks developed parallel to the joint (Figure 2.1A). The same type of deterioration is further advanced in Figure 2.1B. Eventually, concrete near the joint disintegrates and spalls as indicated in Figure 2.1C.

Several theories have been advanced to explain the cause of D-line cracking. One theory holds that concrete deteriorates near the joint in a concrete slab because, as concrete is deposited, fines and mortar are pushed toward the joint and a weaker, more susceptible concrete is placed near the edge. This thory is not supported, however, by the photograph in Figure 2.2A which shows D-line cracking developing along a structural crack in much the same manner as it normally develops along the joint or the edge of a concrete surface.

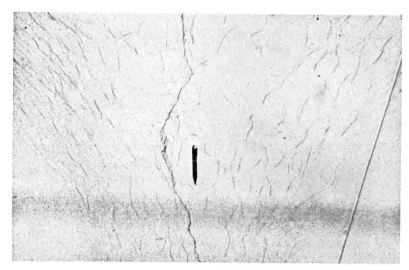

Figure 2.2A—Concrete deterioration starting, with D-line cracks developing along a structural crack.

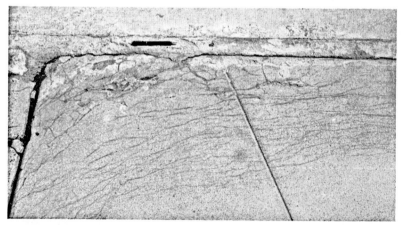

Figure 2.2B—Deterioration originating from D-line cracks progressing from a corner.

A second theory is supported by careful study of field conditions. Concrete next to a joint or a corner is exposed to more moisture than the inside portion of the slab. The concrete adjacent to the joint (as in Figure 2.1A) is exposed to moisture from the crack as it fills with dirt and other moisture-holding debris. Moisture is also available from the base material. Thus the concrete next to a joint or a crack has a higher degree of saturation during freezing weather.

D-line cracks are caused by water as it freezes in the voids of paste and aggregates. When forces become sufficiently great, the tensile strength of the portland cement paste is exceeded and D-line cracks develop along lines of equal saturation, parallel to the joint. As disintegration develops, more water becomes available, through cracks, to feed the capillaries further from the edge of the slab. Progressive development of parallel cracks from the edge or joint of a slab results (Figures 2.2B and 2.2C).

A third theory involving the shape of the concrete specimens may explain the D-line cracking which develops at vertical as well as horizontal corners and edges of rectangular

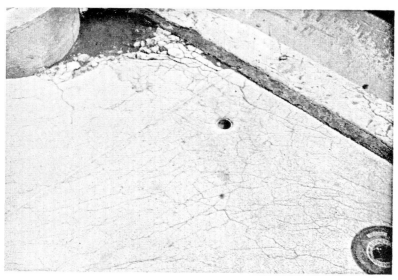

Figure 2.2C—Disintegration spreading to center of a slab.

Figure 2.3A—Over-all view of scaling of service station slab after 6 months exposure. No air entrainment.

pieces. Since spheres of rather mediocre grade concrete have been exposed more than 20 years at Treat Island Exposure Station with practically no deterioration, it has been suggested that stress concentrations which occur at corners and edges when the temperature changes may produce D-line cracking.[5]

## SCALING

Scaling of the surfaces of concrete slabs is one of the most insidious types of deterioration and may occur with slabs of highest quality concrete. Concrete mortar of poor quality will crumble away with repeated freezing and thawing cycles, gradually exposing the coarse aggregate particles. This is a different deterioration mechanism from that which causes the separation of the surface areas of a hard dense slab from interior high quality concrete.

A typical example of scaling is the service station slab shown in Figure 2.3, which was exposed to only a few cycles of freezing and thawing. This slab was constructed in the late fall without entrained air. The concrete used was a 5½-bag mix placed at a slump of 3 to 4 in. Membrane curing compounds were placed on the surface of the slab as soon as it was finished to insure adequate curing. ·Approximately 5 months later scaling occurred as indicated in the photographs. This type of scaling is typical of slabs exposed to severe cold periods before the concrete has had a chance to dry properly after curing. Drying reduces the water in the voids of the concrete below the critical saturation point and limits the moisture available for other deterioration mechanisms. Because this concrete was placed late in the fall and was immediately sealed with a membrane curing compound, it had little opportunity to dry, and the degree of saturation was high during a prolonged cold period.

Several theories can be advanced to explain scaling and each may contribute partially to an explanation of the ultimate failure of concrete surfaces.

1. Pressure developed by expulsion of water from saturated aggregate particles.
2. Hydraulic pressure developed in more numerous capillary cavities just below the concrete surface.
3. Accretion of moisture to ice crystals in capillary voids below the surface.
4. Osmotic pressures caused by concentration of salt in capillaries immediately beneath a concrete surface.[6]
5. Finishing operations which may create a surface condition where the finished surface is dissimilar to the underlying concrete. Improper finishing may also densify the surface and destroy the effectiveness of air entrainment (Figure 4.6).
6. Compaction of the surface by the capillary force of receding water in the surface capillaries óf drying plastic concrete and the subsequent formation of a plane of weakness[7] (Figures 4.5 and 4.7).

7. Additional freezing of subsurface ice crystals caused by melting snow and ice with deicing salts.
8. Replenishment of surface moisture during freezing by melting snow and ice with deicing salts.
9. Cracking and crazing which provides channels for moisture to reach underlying capillary ice (Figure 4.7).

Surface compaction occurs during finishing. It is possible that the concrete was still bleeding when the service station slabs (Figure 2.3B) were finished. Any small amount of additional bleeding which developed after the finish was placed on the concrete accumulated under the compacted surface "skin." This increased the voids immediately under the surface of the slab.

There is evidence that the compaction of the surface of a concrete slab by premature drying may also contribute to scaling of high quality, properly finished concrete. An increase in the quantity of fines, for example, (greater cement content and finer cements) tends to reduce the size of surface capillaries which increases the compacting capillary forces. This may partially explain why coarse-ground earlier cements are considered by some to be more durable.

In support of the compaction theory, one need only to point to the extensive scaling of bridge decks made with modern air-entrained concrete. The concrete of bridge decks is placed on an impermeable base. Excess water must bleed through the full depth of slab to the surface, whereas water in the bottom of slabs can usually escape into a porous base. An impermeable base may, therefore, delay the completion of bleeding until a dried, compacted layer has formed on the surface. A weak, more porous layer may then form just under the surface.

A survey of the extent of scaling on driveways was made recently by the author in Ogden, Utah. In all areas where driveway slabs were placed on a sand base, practically no scaling was found. This included all concrete placed during the last 20 years. In other areas closer to the mountains, where clay strata were exposed, practically every driveway in entire blocks showed severe scaling.

Figure 2.3B—Close-up view of scaling of service station slab reveals removal of a surface "skin."

Figure 2.3C—Concrete below the expansion joint which scaled extensively was placed about 2 to 4 weeks later in the year than the unscaled concrete above. There were no other known differences in these two specimens of non-air-entrained concrete from the same service station slab shown in Figures 2.3A and 2.3B.

One can conclude that saturated concretes with compacted concrete surfaces are vulnerable to scaling. Upon freezing, ice in more numerous capillaries immediately under the surface "skin" grows to such proportions by accretion that the surface of the slab is lifted. An examination of Figure 2.3B indicates that such a mechanism did actually force the surface from the concrete slab. Concrete immediately beneath the scaling was still in sound condition and apparently had not deteriorated.

The only difference between the concrete above the expansion joint, Figure 2.3C, which did not scale and the con-

Figure 2.4—Deterioration of a concrete retaining wall along the saturation line.

crete below the expansion joint which scaled extensively was that the scaled concrete was placed approximately two to four weeks later in the year. The concrete which did not scale may have dried out just enough to reduce the saturation to a point where the mechanism just explained did not occur.

None of the concrete shown in Figure 2.3 contained entrained air. One might logically presume that if the proper amount of air had been entrained in the concrete, the slab would have been protected and scaling would not have occurred. The evidence is against this, however, since similar scaling has been noted in instances where the concrete contained entrained air. Apparently this type of scaling depends upon: (a) the degree of compaction of the surface; (b) the number of capillaries immediately beneath the surface; and (c) the availability of moisture. The laboratory specimen shown in Figure 4.4 shows lenses believed to be caused by the formation of ice in a completely saturated sample of mortar. This indicates that the growth of capillary ice may occur even in a uniform structure of saturated concrete.

## DETERIORATION OF PORTLAND CEMENT PASTE

One of the most common types of freezing and thawing deterioration is the disintegration of the portland cement paste and subsequent exposure of the aggregate particles. Crumbling of the mortar on the surface progresses to the interior of the member.  This type of deterioration can be found at the water line in many early bridge abutments and other hydraulic structures (Figure 2.4).  Deterioration occurs when concrete is saturated above the critical saturation point and then exposed to alternate cycles of freezing and thawing.  Similar deterioration is experienced in the laboratory when specimens are exposed to rapid cycles of freezing and thawing in a saturated condition.  Most structures which show this type of deterioration were built before air entrainment was used in concrete.

## PATTERN CRACKING

Pattern cracking* usually occurs in concrete surfaces which experience either reduced volume at the surface or an increased volume in the interior of the concrete.  Freezing and thawing may cause pattern cracking in the concrete surface by expansion of freezing water either in the voids of the cement paste or in the aggregate pores.

Depletion of gel water during freezing where there is an abundance of air voids suggests the possibility of shrinkage in portland cement paste under freezing conditions.  Prolonged cold periods cause diffusion of water from the gel pores to the air voids and a consequent depletion of the gel pore water. This would tend to cause crazing (fine cracks) in the surface of slabs.

---

* Fine openings (cracks) on concrete surfaces in the form of a pattern.

# 3

## Exposure Conditions
## in Structures

VARYING CONDITIONS OF EXPOSURE for different types of concrete structures have a significant influence on the severity of deterioration that can be anticipated. Maximum vulnerability to damage by freezing exists where moisture in concrete reaches the critical saturation point.

## HYDRAULIC STRUCTURES

The use of hydraulic structures in the transportation and storage of water makes them particularly vulnerable to freezing and thawing simply because there is ample opportunity for portions of these structures to become saturated. Concrete is particularly vulnerable in the range of fluctuating water levels or spray, such as parts of dams, spillways, wasteways, blow-off boxes, tunnel inlets and outlets, tailrace walls, valve houses, canal structures, and other miscellaneous concrete structures. Exposure is also severe in such areas as the tops of walls, tops of boxes, piers, parapets, and all curb sills and ledges, copings, corners, and cornices (Figure 3.1).

Portions of concrete structures where the exposure is less severe include portions of tunnel linings and siphons and the exterior of mass concrete dams and powerhouses.

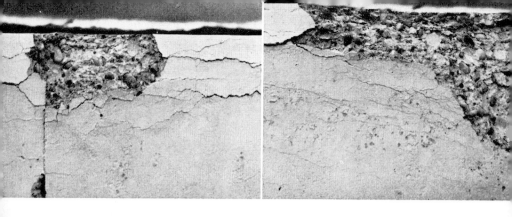

Figure 3.1—Advanced stages of freezing and thawing deterioration in a parapet wall. This wall was placed before the discovery of air entrainment, and was saturated during freezing weather by a water spray mist from the spillway.

Other structures or portions of structures which are covered with sufficient backfill, or which are continually submerged or otherwise protected from the weather, do not present a durability problem. These include parts of dams, trash racks, gate chambers, outlet works, control houses, interiors of tunnels, pipe, and other miscellaneous structures.

## HIGHWAY CONCRETE

Most concrete used in highway work is in pavements, where severe scaling such as that shown in Figures 3.2 and 3.3 may occur. Pavement slabs are subjected to severe freezing and thawing exposure in cold climates. They lie flat on the ground and are exposed to precipitation and subsequent saturation in freezing weather. In addition, highway pavements may be exposed to salts used for snow and ice removal. Pavements must, therefore, be protected against all the mechanisms which produce freezing and thawing deterioration. Specifications usually require low water-cement ratios and air entrainment of about 5 or 6 percent of the volume of concrete. Except for bridge decks, deterioration of pavements due to freezing and thawing has been essentially eliminated since air-entraining admixtures were introduced.

Highway bridges present a serious problem when exposed to freezing and thawing. Most bridges span water courses, and the abutments and piers are in areas of fluctuating water

Figure 3.2—General view of severe scaling of a highway pavement slab.

Figure 3.3—Close-up of the scaling deterioration of pavement shown in Figure 3.2.

levels. This presents the same problem as other hydraulic structures, *i.e.*, the saturation of concrete at the water line. The problem of scaling on bridge decks is widespread. Deterioration is also prevalent on curbs, sills, cornices, and ledges because of their exposure to the elements. Concrete in bridges should, therefore, receive maximum protection from freezing and thawing action.

## CONCRETE IN BUILDINGS

Concrete in most buildings is not subjected to extreme exposure conditions. Most of the concrete in buildings is not exposed to water except for moisture which is blown against the building or falls on the tops of walls, cornices, sills, and ledges during precipitation.

Foundation concrete has little opportunity to become saturated unless the concrete is below the ground water level. In such a case, the concrete is generally protected from freezing temperatures and deterioration is not a problem. Vertical surfaces of foundations which are exposed may become wet during rain storms, but they have little opportunity to reach critical saturation. Interior structural concrete in buildings is not subjected to freezing and thawing deterioration. Building specifications are, therefore, primarily concerned with the strength of the concrete and not its durability.

## SIDEWALKS, DRIVEWAYS, CURBS, AND GUTTERS

Concrete which receives the most severe exposure to freezing and thawing is that which may become saturated during freezing weather, such as gutters, tops of the curbs, sidewalks, or driveways. This type of concrete has the same deterioration problems as highway pavements. Drainage may be provided, but during any period of stormy weather the concrete absorbs water and may reach critical saturation during freezing weather. Specifications for this type of concrete should provide for protection against possible severe exposure.

# 4

# Mechanisms of
# Freezing and Thawing
# Deterioration

THE DETERIORATION OF CONCRETE EXPOSED TO FREEZING AND
THAWING is caused by the expansion of freezing water in the
void system of the cement paste or the concrete aggregates.
Pores in absorptive rock particles are usually large compared
with those in paste. Freezing may damage the paste, leaving
the aggregate undamaged or, conversely, freezing may damage
the aggregate particles while the paste is only indirectly
harmed. Mechanisms which have been advanced to explain
deterioration of the concrete paste or the dilation and break-
age of rock will be discussed.*

## CRITICAL SATURATION

The importance of the degree of saturation and its relation to deterioration was first emphasized in an article which
appeared in *Tonindustrie-Zeitung:*[8]

> The usual method of testing this property
> (durability) consisted of exposing the water-satu-
> rated specimens to a temperature of —15 C and
> allowing it to thaw out, whereupon the procedure
> was repeated until defects were noted or until 24

---

* Most of the theories regarding mechanisms of freezing and thawing deterioration presented here have been advanced by T. C. Powers
and his associates. W. L. Dolch presented additional theories in graduate courses at Purdue University, and research at Utah State University
has expanded certain theories.

23

repetitions proved the resistance of this specimen
by its unharmed condition. The disadvantage of
this method was emphasized by Hirschwalt in a report of the Mineralogical-Berlin, 1910, V. 1, p. 20.
His argument was that water expands by one-tenth
of its volume in changing to ice. When the pores
of the rock are uniformly filled with water to the
extent of nine-tenths, freezing results may complete filling of the pores with no particular pressure, so that the rock remains unchanged by frost
action. Only when saturation is carried beyond
nine-tenths does the ice have insufficient room in
expanding and produces cracks. Hirschwald developed a theory that completely water-soaked
rocks yield to frost action no matter what their
strength while incompletely water-soaked rocks resist this action even when their strength is low. A
rock saturated to nine-tenths of complete saturation was designated by Hirschwald as "incompletely" saturated and it is evident that the commonly accepted test of exposing water-saturated
specimens is too strict for materials which are
never completely soaked by precipitation in nature,
so that many a suitable material is eliminated as
non-resistant to freezing.

The theory of critical saturation is accepted without question. One cubic centimeter of water occupies about 1.09 cc of
space after freezing and any void in the aggregate or cement
paste which is more than 91 percent full of water will be subjected to pressures when freezing water turns to ice, unless the
excess water can be forced from the void during freezing. A
simple illustration of this process is a bottle full of milk which
has frozen on the door step. Either the bottle is broken or the
excess ice formed is pushed out of the mouth of the bottle. If
the milk bottle had been only about 90 percent full, the freezing milk would be accommodated within the bottle. Concrete
deteriorates very rapidly in the freezing and thawing tests if
it is fully saturated.[9]

## STRUCTURE OF PORTLAND CEMENT PASTE

In order to understand the mechanisms of freezing and
thawing within cement paste an understanding of the makeup

of the paste itself is essential. The following explanations were presented by Brunauer,[10] Copeland and Schulz,[11] and Brunauer and Copeland.[12]

Portland cement is a mixture of several compounds, among which the most important ones are two calcium silicates: tricalcium silicate, $Ca_3SiO_2$; and beta-dicalcium silicate, $B-Ca_2SiO_2$. These silicates constitute about 75 percent of the portland cement by weight. In the hydration reaction the two silicates produce similar calcium silicate hydrates and different amounts of calcium hydroxide. The calcium silicate hydrate, because of its similarity to the natural mineral tobermorite,* has been called tobermorite gel. This gel is the most important constituent of hardened portland cement paste and, consequently, also of concrete. Tobermorite gel plays a vital role in determining the rheological properties of fresh portland cement paste. Tobermorite gel also plays a dominant role in the setting and hardening of the paste and in determining the strength and dimensional stability of hardened paste and concrete.

T. C. Powers and his co-workers at the Portland Cement Association were the first to show that two physical properties of cement paste—surface area and porosity—are decisive in determining the two most important engineering properties: strength and dimensional stability.[13] Powers applied the term *cement gel* to the part of hardened paste that is responsible for surface and porosity. The word *gel* signifies an extremely finely divided substance that has a coherent structure.

In addition to surface area and surface force, porosity is also important in determining the strength and dimensional stability of hardened portland cement paste. Inevitably there are tiny pores of molecular dimensions between particles of tobermorite gel, and there are still larger pores between aggregations of gel particles. The former are called gel pores; the latter, capillary pores or cavities. Both are too small to be visible in an ordinary light microscope.

---

* All tobermorites, natural or synthetic, are layer crystals. The natural mineral was found in northern Ireland. Its crystal structure occurs in layers or multiple sheets with some similarities to vermiculite.

The volume of the pore space in a cement paste depends on the amount of water mixed with the cement at the start. When the paste sets, it acquires a stable volume that is approximately equal to the volume of the cement plus the volume of the water. Let us suppose we prepare two pastes from the same cement, using the same amount of cement but different amounts of water. After setting, the paste with the greater amount of water will have the greater volume. After hydration the two pastes will contain the same amounts of solid material, because the same amounts of cement will produce the same amounts of hydration products. The volume of one paste, however, is greater; consequently that paste will have a larger pore space.

This effect has an important influence on the strength of the hardened paste, which is the dominant factor in the strength of concrete. Pores are filled with water and air and they have no strength. The strength is in the solid part of the paste, primarily in the tobermorite.

The less porous paste will produce the stronger concrete. In the mixing of concrete, therefore, no more water should be used than is absolutely necessary.

Copeland and Schulz[11] explain the morphology of tricalcium silicate paste as follows:

> Tricalcium silicate is formed by intermeshed long straight fibers or laths. A close look at these fibers shows them to be either tubular or rolled sheets. The distance across the fibers may be as much as 500 Å,* but their transparency to an electron beam indicates that they are very thin or hollow. The tobermorite (G) formed by paste hydration has a specific surface of approximately 300 $m^2/g$, indicating a mixture of particles two or three layers thick.

The hardened pastes of calcium silicates and portland cements are porous bodies, and changes in relative humidity cause movement of water into or out of the pore system. Entry of water results in swelling, and removal of water, in shrinkage of the paste.

---

* Angstrom, Å, is a unit of length equal to $1 \times 10^{-8}$ cm.

Concrete freezing and thawing deterioration mechanisms occur in the pore structure of portland cement paste and aggregate particles. Knowledge of the submicroscopic pore system of hardened portland cement paste is a prerequisite to an understanding of the phenomenon under discussion. Voids in portland cement paste are classified as follows:

(a) *Gel pores* are the interstitial cavities between the particles of tobermorite and other calcium silicate hydrates. Gel pores are very small and are believed to average approximately 15 to 20 Å in diameter.

(b) *Capillary cavities* are unfilled spaces between aggregations of gel particles. They are formed by uncombined water in excess of that required for hydration of the portland cement. Capillary cavities are estimated to average approximately 5000 Å in diameter.

(c) *Bubbles of entrained air* are much larger and vary from a few microns to a few millimeters in diameter.

Gel pores are generally filled with water in portland cement paste, and if the paste is saturated the capillary cavities will also be filled. However, the gel pores are so small that it is impossible for water to freeze unless the temperature drops far below normal ranges. It is estimated that freezing cannot occur at any temperature above —78 C. Ice crystals cannot form since no more than probably a dozen or so molecules of water can occupy the gel pore. In frozen concrete, therefore, water in the gel pores is supercooled but not frozen. Capillary cavities, on the other hand, are sufficiently large to accommodate ice crystals and water will freeze. Bubbles of entrained air are not generally filled with water unless the concrete becomes saturated by means of vacuum or pressure. These non-coalescing bubbles formed in the plastic concrete mix have sufficient stability to maintain their shape until the concrete is hardened.

When cement gel completely fills the space available to it, the porosity of the gel itself is about 25 percent. From this, one can deduce that the interstitial space in the tobermorite structure is about 25 percent of the over-all volume of hydrated paste. That part of the gross volume which is not filled with the products of hydration has been previously referred to as capillary cavities. The volume of the capillaries depends on the water-cement ratio.

Figure 4.1 is patterned after a similar diagram by Powers and Helmuth.[13] The gel particles and gel pores are indicated as a heterogeneous mass. The larger empty spaces in-

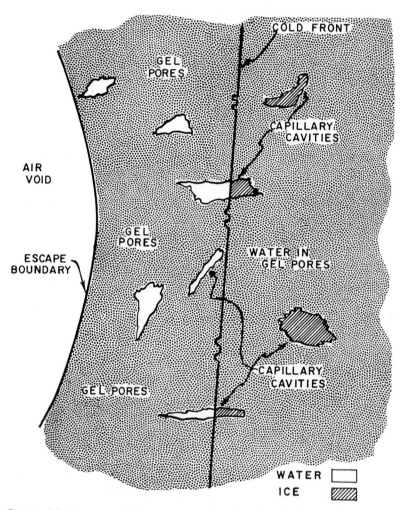

Figure 4.1—Diagram of the pore structure of portland cement paste, based on studies by Powers. If the air void (left) were of average size and drawn to scale, curvature would hardly be discernible in a diagram of this size.

dicate capillary cavities and the curved boundary at the left represents a part of the wall of an air void. It suggests that air voids such as those entrained in concrete are extremely large as compared with the capillary cavities and gel pores in the paste. If the air void were drawn to scale and were of average size the curvature would hardly be discernible.

Capillary cavities are more numerous and larger, the higher the original water-cement ratio and the shorter the period of curing. Ice can exist within the boundaries of the paste only in capillary or air-void cavities. This immediately suggests the benefit of low water-cement ratios in reducing the capillary cavities.

Experimental data show that a very small amount of water freezes near the normal freezing point, but a significant amount of freezing occurs after the temperature falls below the normal freezing temperature. This behavior, as well as other evidence, indicates that most of the capillary cavities are quite small. The surface tension of the bodies of water in capillary cavities puts them under pressure that is higher for the smaller bodies. Hence the smaller the void, the higher the pressure and the lower the freezing point.

## FREEZING IN CAPILLARIES; GENERATION OF HYDRAULIC PRESSURE

In a water-soaked paste the capillary cavities and the gel pores are full, or nearly full of water. When the temperature falls to the point where freezing should begin, ice crystals appear in the largest capillary cavities. When the water in the larger cavities begins to change to ice, the volume of water plus ice will exceed the original capacity of the cavity. Therefore, during the time when the water in the capillaries is changing to ice, the cavity must dilate or the excess water must be expelled from it.

Cement paste is a permeable material, although the coefficient of permeability is extremely low. Hence, there is a possibility that excess water can escape from the capillary during the process of freezing. If one considers the diagram in Figure 4.1 to represent half of the distance between two air voids it can be seen that there is a possibility for the excess water in the capillary to escape to the nearest air void. One may think of the growing ice body in the capillary as a pump forcing the water through the paste toward the void boundary. Such pumping of water involves the generation of pressure. Factors affecting this pressure include:

(a) The coefficient of permeability of the material through which the water is forced.

(b) The distance from the capillary to the void boundary.

(c) The rate at which freezing occurs.

Next consider water freezing in a capillary close to the escape boundary. The excess water can escape from this capillary more readily than from one farther away since resistance to flow is less. In general, during the process of freezing, hydraulic pressure will exist throughout the paste. This pressure will be higher for points farther from an escape boundary. If a point in the paste is sufficiently remote from an escape boundary, the pressure will be high enough to stress the surrounding gel beyond its elastic limit, or beyond its tensile strength, and thus will produce permanent damage.

Every air void in cement paste is assumed to be bordered by a zone in which the hydraulic pressure cannot become high enough to cause damage. Theoretically, pressure increases approximately in proportion to the square of the distance from the void. By reducing the distance between voids to the point where the protected zones overlap, generation of disruptive hydraulic pressures during the freezing of water in the capillaries can be prevented.

Experimental data by Powers and Helmuth[13] have verified this hypothesis. Consider Figure 4.2, for example, which shows that shrinkage takes place before cooling has advanced to the point where the water first starts freezing, and that as freezing continues rapid expansion takes place. Considering a capillary cavity, hydraulic pressure must first appear in this cavity at the instant that freezing begins. The magnitude of the pressure will depend on rate of freezing and the ease with which water is forced from the cavity. Therefore, the specimen as a whole, acted on simultaneously by all similar cavities, should begin to expand at the instant freezing begins, which is indicated by Figures 4.2 and 4.3. No other mechanism presented to date can account for this coincidence of events.

# DIFFUSION OF AND FREEZING OF GEL WATER IN CAPILLARIES

Ice in the capillaries of frozen cement paste is surrounded by unfrozen water in the gel pores. If the gel is saturated, the gel water has the same free energy as that of ordinary water in bulk. There is thermodynamic equilibrium between the gel

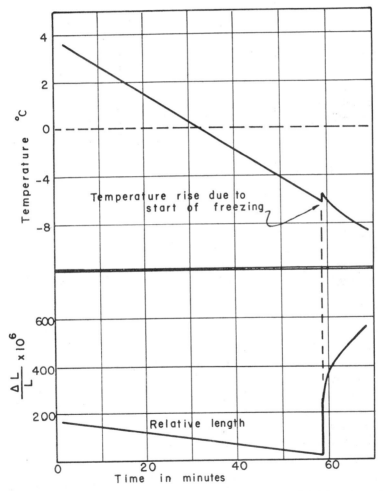

Figure 4.2—Coincidence of initial expansion at the start of freezing. Based on the work of Powers and Helmuth reported in Reference 13.

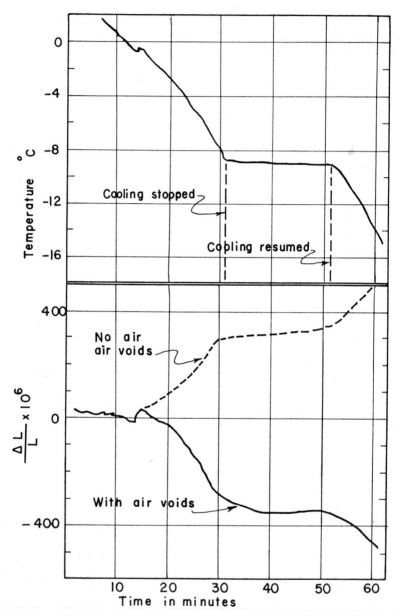

Figure 4.3—Dimensional changes of cement paste with and without air voids, as presented by Powers and Helmuth in 1953 (Reference 13).

water and the ice in the capillary at 0 C, assuming that both the ice and the gel water are under a pressure of one atmosphere and if the capillary is so large as to have negligible surface energy. If the temperature drops below the temperature at which the water in the capillary freezes (assumed to be 0 C) the gel water is no longer in thermodynamic equilibrium with the ice; its free energy is higher than that of the ice. The gel water thus acquires an energy potential enabling it to move into the capillary cavity, where it freezes and causes the ice crystal to grow and enlarge.

The gel has a tendency to shrink as water is diffused from it. On the other hand, the growth of the ice body in the capillary places the ice and the film around the ice under pressure. The swelling pressure in the ice film is enough to produce dilation and expansion of the paste. For example, if the gel were saturated and the capillary cavities contained ice at −5 C, pressure in the film between the ice and the solid gel could be as much as 1200 psi. This amount of pressure would surely cause the paste to dilate appreciably and concrete specimens to expand. This explains why continued expansion occurs in non-air-entrained paste after freezing water in the capillary cavities has expelled the excess water (Figure 4.3).

The question naturally arises whether or not entrained air voids protect the concrete from ice pressures built up in the capillary voids. From the same considerations of thermodynamics it can be seen that gel water will not only diffuse to the capillary cavities, but will also diffuse to ice previously forced into the air voids by hydraulic pressure.

The amount of ice in the air void is not usually equal to the capacity of the void. Consequently, the ice in the air void grows, but may be under no significant pressure. Volume increase of the air-void ice either results in no expansive force at all or at most only a feeble one. The net effect of water lost from the gel to the air void is a tendency to cause shrinkage. The amount of gel water that could enter capillary cavities by diffusion would be a maximum if the paste contained no air voids, and if the boundaries of the specimen were at infinite distance from the cavity. In this case the capillary ice would grow as long as necessary to reach equilibrium with the gel water. If the stress, whether from hydraulic pressure or from subsequent growth of capillary ice, ruptured the gel and thus released the pressure on the ice, the growth would be limited only by the amount of freezable water in the system. On the other hand, if the paste contains air voids, the period of diffusion to the capillary cavities will be correspondingly brief. Laboratory tests verify the assumption regarding the diffusion of gel water and the expansion of specimens after freezing.[13] As already mentioned, rapid expansion with freez-

Figure 4.4—Voids in a laboratory specimen left by ice lenses which formed after six cycles of prolonged freezing (60 hr) and rapid thawing. The 1:2.75 mortar specimen was completely saturated at all times.

ing shown in Figures 4.2 and 4.3 seems to be explainable only in terms of the hydraulic pressure generated during the freezing of capillary water. In Figure 4.2 the first rising part of the curve represents expansion due to hydraulic pressure. Expansion due to diffusion of gel water to the capillaries is shown by the dotted line in Figure 4.3. The influence of air voids is shown by the bottom curve of Figure 4.3.

It should also be pointed out that an outside source of moisture which may replenish the gel water during a thawing cycle, through cracks or fractures (crazing cracks), will theoretically provide moisture for unlimited growth of the ice crystals. The photograph (Figure 4.4) shows voids left by ice lenses which developed in saturated mortar after prolonged freezing periods interrupted by rapid thawing.

## OSMOTIC PRESSURES

When solutions of different concentrations of soluble materials are separated by a permeable barrier, the solvent particles move through the barrier toward the solution of greater concentration and a differential head is set up between the two solutions. This osmotic action increases the hydraulic pressure in cement paste as freezable water is forced from the capillaries into the gel pores.

Assume the water in the capillary cavities of cement paste contains a concentration of salts or alkalies. This concentration increases as the water begins to freeze, and the water being forced from the capillaries will have a higher concentration of salt than the surrounding gel pore water. A pressure differential develops in the direction toward the capillary pore and opposite to the flow of water. The pressure required to overcome osmotic pressure in the capillary is a combination of the hydraulic pressure required to force capillary water into the gel pore structure plus the osmotic pressure which resists this flow.

This mechanism has been suggested as a possible cause of scaling of concrete pavements where salt is used. Placing salt on pavements for ice removal will increase the concentration of salt in the capillary voids near the surface of the pavement. As the salt solution freezes, a greater concentration of salt results and osmotic pressure is built up in the capillary cavities. This increase in pressure may be sufficient to cause a rupture of the cement gel near the surface of the pavement, and consequently cause scaling.

Experimentation by Verbeck and Klieger[6] shows that an increase in the concentration of salt in freezing and thawing tests increases the disruptive effect of freezing and thawing. Concentrations from 2 to 4 percent appear to cause the greatest deterioration of concrete due to the optimum combination of freezable water and osmotic pressure. If the concentration increases above 4 percent, there is a decrease in deterioration. The higher concentration of salt may lower the freezing temperature of the salt solution, which would give the water in the capillary cavities an antifreeze effect and reduce the freezable water. The use of salt may also increase the concentration in the pore structure of surface concrete to a point where the salt solution would act as an antifreeze and increase the availability of moisture for saturation of the concrete.

## SCALING MECHANISMS

The surface of a concrete slab is artificially compacted by finishing. Steel troweling produces a hard, dense, abrasion-resistant surface desirable in heavy duty floors. Such a finish in a slab exposed to freezing and thawing may lead to surface scaling.

The mechanism involved is best illustrated by a natural phenomenon shown in Figure 4.5. When fresh concrete re-

**WATER SURFACE**

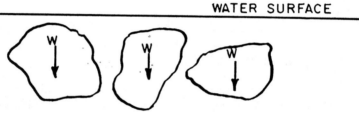

As long as a film of bleed water covers the cement grains the only compacting force is the weight of the solid grains less the weight of water $W = W_s - W_w$.

As the bleed water disappears, capillary pressure ($P = P_2 - P_1$) is added to the compacting forces. $P = 2T/R$, where $T =$ surface tension and $R =$ radius of the meniscus.

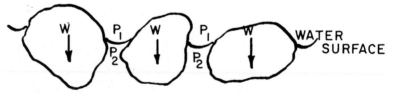

Figure 4.5—Compacting forces caused by rapid drying of fresh concrete.

Figure 4.6—These two views of a piece of broken concrete (above) and of the top of a 6x12-in. cylinder (bottom) show evidence of a compacted surface with a more porous zone beneath. Note the void over a coarse aggregate particle.

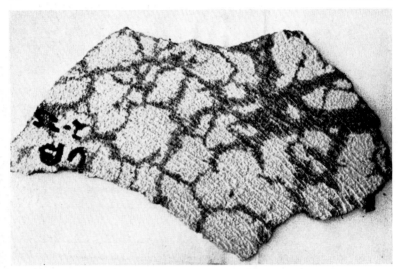

Figure 4.7—Moisture channels which feed subsurface capillaries. Result of placing a 4x8-in. piece of scaled concrete in a pan with water covering the bottom (surface up).

Same piece of concrete (below) placed in pan of water with slab surface down. Moisture pattern appeared immediately.

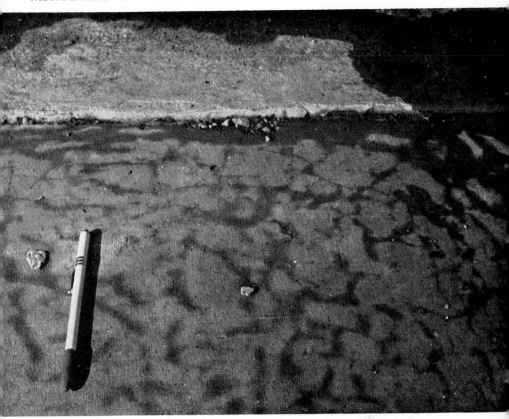

Figure 4.8—Corner of a sidewalk slab in the process of drying out. Moisture channels to the surface are apparent.

mains in a plastic state the greater density of the particles of aggregate and portland cement will cause them to settle and the lighter water will tend to rise to the surface. This phenomenon, known as "bleeding," creates a film of water on freshly placed concrete (Figure 4.5). As long as this water film is on the surface the only natural compacting force is the force of gravity. Rapid drying of the surface moisture may lower the water level so that particles of cement and aggregate are exposed as indicated in Figure 4.5. At this point further lowering of the water surface is resisted by capillary forces in the surface voids among the particles of solids. The magnitude of the capillary forces depends on the size of the capillary and the length of the tube. These forces are significant, however, and may result in a compacting force computed to be from 500 to 1400 psf.[7, 14] Concrete immediately beneath the surface is not subjected to these capillary forces and is, therefore, not compacted. Moreover, if this mechanism develops before the concrete has set, bleeding water will continue to rise but will be trapped beneath the compacted surface layer.

This mechanism creates a dense surface layer on concrete pavements with a less dense layer immediately beneath it, as indicated in the photographs of Figure 4.6. The only condition lacking to separate the compacted surface from the pavement in freezing weather is sufficient moisture to permit the growth of capillary ice in the porous layer.

The mechanism of accretion previously discussed will provide for continued growth of the ice crystals as long as moisture is available. Fine crazing cracks through a dense, dried, compacted surface layer provide ideal access channels for surface moisture (Figure 4.7). Deicing salts not only create additional forces through osmosis, but also provide an additional source of surface moisture in freezing weather by melting the ice and snow. As snow and ice are melted by deicing salts, the temperature immediately below the surface is reduced significantly because of the comparatively large heat of fusion of ice. This may cause a damaging temperature drop in the saturated zone immediately beneath the surface.[15]

Thus deicing salts may cause concrete to scale by any combination of the following:

1. By providing moisture from the melting of ice and snow in freezing weather
2. By causing additional freezing through lowering the temperature in the subsurface zone (ice cream freezer principle)
3. By creating a system which develops osmotic pressures
4. By a buildup of salt crystals in subsurface voids.

It is not surprising, therefore, that severe scaling has occurred in high quality pavements only a few months old.

It is the consensus that more extensive scaling appears on concrete pavement slabs which are placed in the fall or early winter just before prolonged cold periods.

There are several explanations why new concrete is more susceptible to scaling than old concrete:

1.  Partially hydrated portland cement paste contains more capillary voids.
2.  Partially hydrated paste has a greater degree of saturation since portland cement draws water from adjacent capillaries as it hydrates.
3.  In addition to dimensional changes due to drying shrinkage and thermal contraction, additional shrinkage results from the diffusion of unused water in the gel structure to the capillaries. This is undoubtedly another cause of crazing of new concrete in cold weather.
4.  New concrete has less strength and therefore has less resistance to the disruptive forces of freezing.

# 5

# Influence of
# Concrete Aggregates

THE LACK OF DURABILITY OF CONCRETE caused by deterioration
of the portland cement paste under exposure to freezing and
thawing has been discussed. Concrete may also deteriorate
when exposed to freezing and thawing because of mechanisms within the concrete aggregate particles. Concrete aggregate particles contain pores of various sizes and characteristics. Lewis and Dolch[16] point out that the behavior of aggregate particles when exposed to freezing and thawing depends primarily upon the pore structure, permeability, and the
degree of saturation of the aggregate particle. The most important aggregate properties that are influenced by freezing
and thawing are the pore size distribution and permeability.
Since the permeability is controlled by the size and continuity
of the pores, these two porosity characteristics may be considered the most important. The total porosity is of secondary
importance. Lewis and Dolch[16] describe the lack of durability
of concrete aggregates in freezing and thawing as follows:

> The lack of durability of an aggregate in freezing
> and thawing is primarily dependent upon its abil-
> ity to become and stay highly saturated under the‑

given conditions of exposure. The harmful pore size is large enough to permit water readily to enter much of the pore space but not large enough to permit easy drainage.

The pressure exerted by freezing water (if no expansion or escape of water is possible) ranges up to 2900 psi at −4 F. Pressures in this range may develop in aggregate particles when the saturation is critical. To avoid development of pressures in excess of the tensile strength of either the aggregate particles or the surrounding mortar, the pore water must be able to flow into unfilled pores or escape from the particle. Escape from the particle may be blocked by a frozen zone around the outside resulting in the development of high pressure in the interior. Even when flow away from the freezing zone is possible, hydraulic pressure is necessary to cause movement through small voids and may be so high as to cause fracture of the material. It is estimated that pores less than four microns in diameter will drain effectively only at pressures high enough to cause some rock or concrete failures.

The aggregate particle itself need not fail in order for the concrete in which it is used to suffer damage from freezing and thawing. Aggregates may have enough strength and elasticity to withstand the stresses without failure, but the surrounding mortar may be damaged by the expansion of the aggregate particle. Freezing and thawing tests of samples of aggregate alone may not be indicative of the durability of concrete. The rate at which water must escape from the freezing zone and the pressure required to cause such flow depend on the rate of freezing and the permeability of the material. A hypothesis of this nature for the effect of freezing and thawing on pastes has been discussed and is similar to what might be expected in concrete aggregates.

Four mechanisms explain deterioration of concrete aggregates and deterioration of concrete containing questionable aggregates.

## ELASTIC ACCOMMODATION

Critical saturation of the voids is just as important in aggregates as in portland cement paste. If the porosity of a

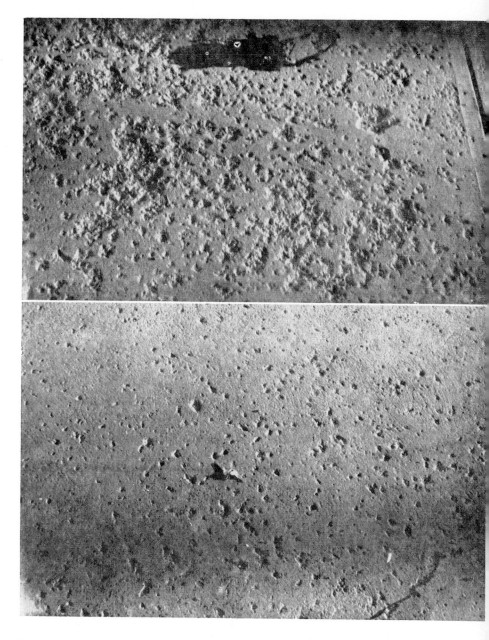

Figure 5.1—Severe popout deterioration caused by inferior shale aggregate.

rock is such that it can accommodate expansion of water when it freezes, the particle is not fractured and does not expand. In cases where the saturation of an aggregate particle is greater than the critical saturation, it is possible that the elastic strain within the rock structure itself may accommodate the expansion as water freezes to ice.

Most aggregate particles have much greater tensile strength than portland cement paste. It is possible, therefore, that some aggregates may be able to withstand comparatively high pressures within the aggregate particle without fracturing. As the pressures increase, the aggregate particle may expand elastically and accommodate the increased volume of ice. The surrounding concrete paste may not be able to withstand such expansion, and thus the aggregate can cause deterioration of the paste even though it is not fractured. Much depends upon the number and size of pores within the aggregate particle and the strength and modulus of elasticity of the aggregate. Some pores within the aggregate particle may act in the same manner as entrained air bubbles and provide escape boundaries for the increase in pressure within the pore structure of the aggregate particle.

## CRITICAL SIZE OF THE AGGREGATE

The pore structure of some rocks is such that water is absorbed by the aggregate particle and when frozen this water will be forced to the outside surface. Other rocks have pore space within the rock itself similar to entrained air bubbles. If one assumes that water which is forced from the void as freezing takes place must find its way to the outside surface of the rock, the size of the rock itself becomes critical.[17] Water forced for short distances would develop low hydraulic pressures which would increase as the distance increases. The critical size of aggregate therefore depends on:

(a) Freezing rate
(b) Degree of saturation
(c) Permeability.

The permeability of a rock determines the critical size in two ways. First, high permeability allows more water to be absorbed in a given period of time. On the other hand, however, it permits the water to be expelled from the particle more rapidly without developing high pressures.

Experience has shown that very porous rocks do not deteriorate when exposed to freezing and thawing; they allow the ingress and egress of water rapidly enough so that internal pressures do not develop. Rocks with relatively fine pores, on the other hand, are more susceptible to fracturing unless the rock particles are small enough that their size is not critical.

Rocks such as cherts and shales and some limestones are susceptible to fracturing when frozen in a saturated condition. These types cause popouts in the surfaces of concrete. In each popout a fractured rock of comparatively high absorption and fine pores will be found in the bottom (Figures 5.1 and 5.2).

## ACCRETION OF WATER FROM SURROUNDING PASTE

Some rocks have the property of drawing water from an outside source as ice crystals start to build, similar to the growth of ice in the capillaries of portland cement. This is considered to be of relatively minor importance, however, since the differential of free energy between the gel water in cement paste and the ice crystals within the aggregate particle would undoubtedly be limited to that portion of the surface of the rock immediately adjacent to the cement gel. Any aggregate particles which have a strong affinity for water would readily absorb the available water, and it is believed that other mechanisms play more important roles in deterioration of rocks than the possible effect of growth of ice crystals within the aggregate particle itself.

## EXPULSION OF WATER FROM CONCRETE AGGREGATES INTO PORTLAND CEMENT PASTE

When saturated aggregate particles are frozen, the increase in the volume during the formation of ice must be accommodated either within the aggregate particle itself or forced into the surrounding cement paste. Trouble from this mechanism will occur around the periphery of the aggregate particle and there must be sufficient entrained air bubbles in the paste not only to accommodate the expulsion of water from the capillaries of the paste, but also to accommodate the water which is expelled from the aggregate particle. The degree of saturation of the aggregate is critical since water will not be forced from the aggregate particle unless saturation is greater than 91 percent.

Highly porous rocks, such as reef rock or porous sandstones, have pore sizes so large that there is no danger of de-

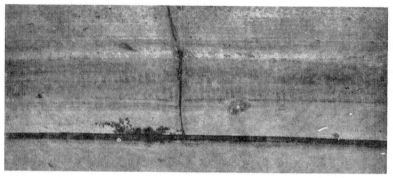

Figure 5.2—Popout in new concrete caused by a small pebble of chert.

terioration from freezing and thawing. Water is absorbed readily by these rocks, but in the freezing and thawing cycle, permeability is sufficient that pressure is not built up within the rock during freezing. All excess water is forced from the aggregate particle.

Rocks with medium fine pores absorb water quite rapidly, but the permeability is also sufficient that the water can be forced from the aggregate particle before building up pressures. Rocks of this type will cause more trouble by expulsion of the excess water into the surrounding paste and may cause popouts or expansion cracks.

Rocks of very fine pores do not saturate rapidly, but they do become highly saturated and absorb large amounts of water. Claystones, siltstones, cherts, and shales are very susceptible to popouts (Figures 5.1 and 5.2). Upon freezing, excessive pressures are built up within the rock particle causing it to expand and fracture the concrete to the surface.

Limitation of absorption is probably the simplest specification method of reducing freezing and thawing difficulties caused by aggregates. Experience has shown that concrete does not deteriorate because of poor aggregates with low absorption, whereas concrete, even though protected by air entrainment, may deteriorate if it contains aggregates of high absorption.

# 6

## Air Entrainment

THE UNIVERSAL ACCEPTANCE OF ENTRAINED AIR in concrete attests to the benefits to be derived from its use. Superior resistance to freezing and thawing damage is unquestioned after two decades of experience. Its use is generally mandatory under conditions of severe natural weathering. ACI Committee 212, Admixtures for Concrete, provides the following information regarding air-entraining admixtures.

### EFFECTS OF AIR ENTRAINMENT

The benefits of air entrainment have been described in many articles.[3, 4, 18, 19] Experience has demonstrated the superior durability of air-entrained concrete. Its use should always be required under conditions of severe natural weathering and where sodium chloride or calcium chloride is used for ice removal on pavements. Air-entrained concrete containing a large number of very small air bubbles is several times as resistant to frost action as non-air-entrained concrete made of the same materials, but air-entrained concrete should be a dense, impermeable mixture that is well placed, protected, finished, and cured if maximum durability is to be obtained.

Air entrainment materially alters the properties of both the freshly mixed and the hardened concrete. Air-entrained concrete is considerably more plastic and workable than non-air-entrained concrete. It can be handled and placed with less segregation and there is less tendency for bleeding. The durability of the hardened concrete is improved by increased uniformity, decreased absorption and permeability, and by the elimination of planes of weakness at the top of lifts. These effects are due to a change in the characteristics of the concrete brought about by the presence of a large number of minute air bubbles in the paste. At a given air content, the protection afforded by the voids against damage by freezing and thawing usually is greater, the larger the number of voids per unit volume of paste. This means that the voids are more effective when they are closer together.[20, 21, 22] The cement paste in concrete is normally protected against the effects of freezing and thawing if the spacing factor[21] of the air void system is 0.008 in. or less as determined in accordance with ASTM C 457, but for some conditions a maximum spacing factor less than 0.008 in. may be required.[22]

The air content and the size distribution of air voids produced in air-entrained concrete are influenced by many factors,[21] among the more important of which are: (1) the nature and concentration of the air-entraining admixture; (2) nature and proportions of the constituents of the concrete mixture; (3) type and duration of mixing employed; (4) consistency; and (5) kind and degree of compaction applied in placing the concrete.

The use of air entrainment does not vitiate the need for control of the water-cement ratio. As the water-cement ratio is increased, the average size of the air voids, the distance between the air voids, and the freezable water content of the cement paste increase under given conditions, resulting in decreased resistance of the concrete to freezing and thawing. Resistance of concrete to laboratory freezing and thawing has not been found to be affected adversely by loss of air as a result of vibration, provided that the concrete originally contained an adequate void system. Presumably the same is true of frost resistance under field conditions.

Air entrainment, while improving both workability and durability, may reduce strength. Within the range of air content normally used, the decrease in strength usually is about proportional to the amount of air entrained. For most types of exposed concrete a slight reduction in strength is far less significant than the improved resistance to frost action. The reduction in strength rarely exceeds 15 percent in the case of compressive strength and 10 percent in the case of flexural strength. These figures are based on comparison with non-air-entrained concrete of equal cement content, and with the sand and water content of the air-entrained concrete reduced to the extent permitted by the increased workability of this type of mixture.

The discussion above refers to the use of moderate amounts of entrained air, usually not more than 13 percent by volume of the mortar fraction of the concrete. In some applications of concrete, particularly in precast units, much greater quantities of entrained air are employed to produce lightweight products with superior thermal insulating properties.

## AIR-ENTRAINING MATERIALS USED AS ADMIXTURES

Many materials, including natural wood resins, fats, and oils may be used in preparing air-entraining admixtures. These materials are usually insoluble in water and generally must be chemically processed before they can be used as admixtures.

Since not all such materials produce a desirable air void system, air-entraining admixtures should meet the requirements of ASTM C 260, specifications for air-entraining admixtures for concrete. Conformance with these specifications will assure that the admixture functions as an air-entraining agent, that it can effect a substantial improvement in the resistance of concrete to freezing and thawing, and that none of the essential properties of the concrete (*e.g.*, strength, volume change) is seriously impaired.

## AIR-ENTRAINING CEMENT

Air-entrained concrete can also be made by using an air-entraining portland cement. Air-entraining portland cement is portland cement that contains one or more air-entraining additions (see ASTM C 219) which have been interground with it during manufacture. Air-entraining cement should be required to meet the ASTM specification for air-entraining portland cement, C 175.

## PREPARATION OF AIR-ENTRAINED CONCRETE

At present both methods of entraining air are being used extensively and both are providing improved concrete. Adding the admixture at the mixer is preferred because the air content can be controlled within close limits or can be changed readily as may be indicated by the requirements of the work. Air-entraining cement may be preferred because it is convenient, and affords some assurance of increased durability even when facilities are not available to measure the resulting air content. ACI 613–54, "Recommended Practice for Selecting Proportions for Concrete," should be followed in either case.

Regardless of the method of air entrainment employed in the preparation of air-entrained concrete, the properties of the concrete-making materials, the proportioning of the concrete mixture, and all aspects of the mixing, handling, and placing procedures should be maintained as constant as feasible so that the air content of the concrete will be uniform and within the range specified for the work. The air content of the concrete should be checked and controlled during the course of the work in accordance with the recommendations of ACI Committee 611 as reported in the ACI *Manual of Concrete Inspection*. Particular attention should be given to the unusually high amount of air-entraining admixture often required in concrete containing high-early-strength (Type III) portland cement, portland-pozzolan cements, fly ash, finely divided mineral admixtures such as natural pozzolans, or finely divided coloring admixtures such as untreated carbon black.

When accelerators and water-reducing, set-retarding admixtures are used, some air-entraining admixtures are not compatible with these other admixtures if intermixed prior to addition to the concrete and so must be added separately to the batch. The manufacturer's recommendations should be followed in such instances.

The air content, spacing factor, and other significant parameters of the air void system in hardened concrete can be determined microscopically by several methods, the most commonly used being the linear traverse and modified point-count procedures as described in ASTM C 457. These methods afford means to determine the air content and characteristics of the air void system in concrete of structures. Use of these methods in coordination with investigations of proportioning of concrete for new projects provides greater assurance that concrete of satisfactory resistance to freezing and thawing will be obtained.

## Air-Entraining Agents

ACI Committee 212 indicates that many materials will entrain air in concrete. One story of the discovery of air entrainment attributes it to bearings leaking grease into cement in the grinding mills of a cement plant. Consequent production of "air-entraining cement" with resulting improvement in durability, led to further research.

Although many organic materials will entrain air in concrete, there are only three general types in extensive commercial use:

(a) Wood resins
(b) Detergents
(c) Sulfonated hydrocarbons of petroleum.

ASTM C 494-62T specifications for chemical admixtures designates vinsol resin (very insoluble resin) as a control air-entraining agent. This product has the disadvantage of being insoluble in water and must be neutralized with caustic soda. The preparation of an aqueous solution is difficult. Other wood resins are readily soluble in water and can be mixed on the job. Approximately 5 to 25 grams of various dry agents is required to entrain sufficient air in 1 cu yd of concrete. Wood resins and detergents sell for 10 to 30 cents a pound, which makes the cost of air entrainment negligible.

Since only minute quantities of a dry air-entraining agent are required to entrain the recommended volume of air in concrete, it is more desirable to batch a dilute water solution in a concrete mix. Agents are added at concentrations of 4 to 12 percent, agent to water. Even at these concentrations, only a fraction of an ounce may be required per sack of cement.

## Dispensers

Various types of dispenser controls are in use, including volumetric measurement, timed flow, flow meters, and revolutions of a positive displacement pump.

A positive displacement pump calibrated into an automatic batching plant provides a positive and automatic method for batching admixtures. A suitable check for faulty operation is necessary, however, for any dispensing method.

## MEASUREMENT OF ENTRAINED AIR IN CONCRETE

The percentage of entrained air in concrete must be carefully controlled since the freezing and thawing durability is impaired if the concrete contains an insufficient amount of air, and strength is unnecessarily reduced if the percentage of air becomes excessive.

Three common methods[23] used to make air content determinations are the volumetric method, the gravimetric method, and the pressure method.

## Volumetric Method

In this case the volume of air is released from the concrete and measured directly. This is usually accomplished by mixing a known volume of water with a known volume of concrete, agitating the mixture until the air separates from the slurry, and measuring the decrease in total volume.

## Gravimetric (Unit Weight) Method

The weight of a unit volume of concrete varies inversely with the amount of air entrained. The percentage of air can be simply determined:

$$\text{percent air} = \frac{W_c - W_{ac}}{W_c} \times 100$$

where $W_c$ = unit weight of concrete without air, and $W_{ac}$ = unit weight of air-entrained concrete.

## Pressure Method

The pressure method is based on the well-known pressure-volume relationship of Boyle's law:

$$PV = P^1V^1$$

Air which has been pumped to a predetermined pressure in a compartment of known volume is released into a sealed container full of concrete. From the decrease in pressure, the volume of the air voids which caused the pressure decrease can be computed. Commercial testing apparatus are calibrated to read air percentage directly.

Another version of the pressure method, ASTM C 231-62, measures the decrease in volume of air-entrained concrete subjected to a given pressure. These meters are also calibrated to read air percentage directly.

The pressure method is the most widely used method of measuring air, principally because of the accuracy and speed of making the tests. One disadvantage of the pressure method is that it also measures the volume of the unfilled voids in the aggregate. Because of the large percentage of voids in light-weight aggregate particles, the volumetric method is more accurate in measuring the entrained air content of lightweight concrete. The pressure method can be used with lightweight aggregate concrete to measure the entrained air (added) by measuring the air content of a mix without air-entraining agents and also one in which agents were added.

$$A_E = A_o - A_{AEA}$$

where $A_E$ = entrained air; $A_o$ = measured air in original mix without air-entraining agents; and $A_{AEA}$ = measured air in air-entrained mix.

Added air content may also be determined from batch weights and the unit weight of concrete.

$$V_{ba} = \frac{\Sigma \text{ batch weights, lb}}{\text{unit weight of air-entrained concrete, lb per cu ft}}$$

$$V_b = \frac{\Sigma \text{ batch weights, lb}}{\text{unit weight of regular concrete, lb per cu ft}}$$

$$\text{added air (cu ft)} = V_{ba} - V_b; \text{ added air (percent)} = \frac{V_{ba} - V_b}{V_{ba}}$$

where $V_{ba}$ = volume of a batch of concrete containing an air-entraining agent, cu ft; and $V_b$ = volume of a batch of concrete without an air-entraining agent, cu ft.

The amount of air *added* to lightweight concrete is of greater significance than the total volume of air in the mix. When $V_b$ is established for a given concrete mix $V_{ba}$ can be used to not only check the yield of the batch in cubic feet, but also to check the air content.

## FACTORS WHICH INFLUENCE AIR ENTRAINMENT IN CONCRETE

The quantity of air entrained by a given quantity of air-entraining agent is influenced by many variables as shown in Table 6.1. Any variable which tends to increase the foaming action of an air-entraining agent will increase the amount of entrained air. For example, it is more difficult to entrain air in stiff concrete and conversely, if the slump is too high (excess of water) the air may be mixed out of the concrete before it is placed.

### TABLE 6.1—FACTORS WHICH INFLUENCE AIR ENTRAINMENT

| Tend to increase air content | Tend to decrease air content |
|---|---|
| Cool temperature | Increase in very fine material cement, pozzolan, silt, etc. |
| Increase in fine sand, 30- to 50- mesh sizes | Rise in temperature |
| Increase in slump up to 7 in. | Decrease in slump |
| Decrease in quantity of cement, pozzolan, or silt | Very high slump (8 in.) |
| Use of other admixtures | Low sand percentage |
| High sand percentage | Coarse sand |

The 30–50 size range of sand is most effective in entraining air in a concrete mix.[4] Very fine materials reduce the amount of air entrained and coarser sizes do not provide the required foaming action. Some "sand-gravel" aggregates, which have an excess of the medium sizes of sand, are of such a grading that they naturally produce over 2 percent air without the addition of air-entraining agents. Although foaming agents are usually more effective in hot water than cold, an increase in temperature of concrete increases the chemical activity of the portland cement with an increase in water requirement of the mix. A decrease in air content usually results.

Very fine materials have a dampening effect on the foaming action and reduce the air content. Some fly ash pozzolans contain carbon which absorbs the organic air-entraining agent before it can entrain air in the concrete. A significant increase in the quantity of agent is sometimes necessary.

# 7

# Laboratory Evaluation
# of Freezing and Thawing
# Deterioration

THE SEVERAL FREEZING AND THAWING MECHANISMS which cause deterioration in concrete do not operate under the same climatic conditions. For example, rapid freezing and thawing is unusually severe in developing hydraulic pressure in the gel structure, but is too rapid to permit the buildup of ice crystals due to accretion. Moreover, laboratory specimens which are tested submerged in water are more likely to reach critical saturation than exposed structures in the field. It is difficult, therefore, to establish standard testing procedures which properly evaluate freezing and thawing resistance for all field conditions.

Table 7.1 gives a brief summary of several test methods currently in use. The four ASTM methods require that freezing and thawing tests be started after 24 hr of moist curing in the fog room followed by immersion in water saturated with lime to the age of test. The Corps of Engineers method C-10-54 has a similar requirement except that storage is in the fog room until 48 ± 4 hr prior to test when they are stored in saturated lime water. None of these methods provides for preliminary drying of the concrete.

Each of the test methods listed has certain weaknesses and strong points, and it would be presumptuous to say that one method is superior to all others.

ASTM C 290, rapid freezing and thawing in water, is used more extensively than any other method. This method is severe and in a comparatively short time will indicate the relative quality of portland cement paste and/or aggregates. The test provides a useful tool, therefore, in discriminating among proposed materials for use in concrete. Perhaps the actual exposure conditions in the field are of secondary importance for this purpose.

#### TABLE 7.1—FREEZING AND THAWING TEST METHODS

| Test method | Type of specimen | Measure of deterioration | Type of exposure |
|---|---|---|---|
| ASTM C 290 | 3x3x15-in. prism | Loss in dynamic $E$ | Rapid freezing and thawing in water |
| ASTM C 291 | 3x3x15-in. prism | Loss in dynamic $E$ | Rapid freezing in air and thawing in water |
| ASTM C 292 | 3x3x15-in. prism | Loss in dynamic $E$ | Slow freezing and thawing in water or brine |
| ASTM C 310 | 3x3x15-in. prism | Loss in dynamic $E$ | Slow freezing in air and thawing in water |
| Corps of Engineers C-10-54 | 3½x4½x16-in. prism | Loss in dynamic $E$ | Rapid freezing and thawing in air and in water |
| USBR method | 3x6-in. cylinder | Expansion and weight loss | Rapid freezing and thawing in water |
| Powers method | 4½x9-in. cylinder | Expansion | Controlled freezing |

The USBR method of determining weight loss of 3x6-in. cylinders may not be realistic as a quantitative indication of freezing and thawing resistance in the field, but many thousands of tests have been correlated with actual service records on numerous projects. With this background information, tests on a particular sample can be interpolated for an indication of actual field service.

## TEST METHOD SIMULATES FIELD CONDITIONS

Recently an effort has been made to duplicate field exposure conditions in evaluating the suitability of local aggregates for use in concrete. The test method, designated here as Powers method, was outlined by Tremper and Spellman[24] after extensive tests in evaluating aggregates for the California Highway Department. The theoretical mechanisms previously discussed, which were advanced by T. C. Powers, were evaluated. Points made by Powers are given below, and the test procedures used to implement his concepts are described.

### Size of Aggregate

There is a critical size of aggregate with respect to its frost resistance. In general, the larger its size the greater its probability of being vulnerable. Therefore, test specimens should contain the largest size of aggregate to be used in the work, and the dimensions of the specimen should be adequate for this purpose.

Specifications for the California projects under consideration required that the concrete contain 1½ in. maximum size aggregate. This size range was used in preparing laboratory mixtures for test. Cylinders with a diameter of 4½ in. and 9 in. high were molded for the Powers test. While it might have been possible to consolidate specimens of smaller size, the number of the large size particles of aggregate in each specimen would have been reduced. Since the larger particles are more likely to be the critical ones, it was not thought advisable to use a smaller test specimen. Specimens for ASTM rapid freezing and thawing in water were 4x5x18-in. prisms, on which dynamic $E$ was measured, or 4½x9-in. cylinders, on which length changes were measured.

## Moisture in Aggregates

Aggregates dug from locations below the water table and subsequently allowed to dry may not regain their full amount of water by simple soaking for a resonable length of time. If the aggregates as incorporated in test concrete are not saturated to a degree comparable to the condition in which they are used in the work, the test results can be very misleading.

Specifications required that aggregates be washed before use. In practice, aggregates are usually dug, screened, washed, and batched without any opportunity for drying. Preliminary test samples of pit run material were taken below the water table. Samples from manufactured stocks were taken only where free surface moisture was visible. They were placed in metal cans with tight fitting covers. Additional water was placed in each can. In the laboratory, the aggregates were maintained in a thoroughly wet condition during screening and other processing and were introduced into the mixer while wet. It might have been possible to resaturate dried aggregates under vacuum, but uncertainty as to completeness of saturation led to the adoption of the first procedure.

## Air Bubble Spacing

For tests of air-entrained concrete, the paste should be protected with bubbles, and adequate protection requires that the calculated spacing factor not exceed 0.01 in.*

The laboratory was not equipped to make linear traverse measurements of polished sections. It was assumed that the use of neutralized vinsol resin in an amount to result in a measured air content of 4.5 ± 0.5 percent would fulfill the bubble spacing requirement.

## Rate of Cooling

The rate of cooling in a laboratory test should not be greatly higher than the rate experienced under natural condi-

---

* This factor is 0.008 according to ACI Committee 212.

tions of exposure. The use of high cooling rates in the laboratory as required in some current methods subjects the concrete to internal hydraulic pressures much greater than experienced in nature and may produce misleading results. Such a test may serve to reject aggregates that would be satisfactory in service.

Prior to starting tests, an experimental slab 12-ft square had been installed with thermocouples at Donner Pass, the highest elevation of the proposed construction. Temperature measurements were recorded during one winter. In the range below 32 F, the greatest rate of temperature drop within the concrete did not exceed 3 F per hr except on one day when a drop of 6 F in 1 hr was recorded at a point just below the surface of the slab. Powers has suggested a cooling rate in the test of 5 F per hr and this rate was adopted in the work.

## Moisture in Concrete

Unless the concrete is to be exposed in such a way that it will never have an opportunity to dry, it will dry to some extent during each summer season. Concrete specimens should be conditioned by partial drying to a degree comparable to field conditions before subjecting them to freezing.

The method proposed is to determine the change in length of concrete while it is being slowly cooled below normal freezing point. If the concrete shrinks normally in the freezing range, it is immune to frost at the time of test. If it dilates, it is not immune and the process that eventually causes disintegration has begun.

## CONSENSUS ON FREEZING AND THAWING TESTS

Standard laboratory tests used for measuring freezing and thawing deterioration of concrete provide valuable tools in discriminating among concrete materials. Direct comparisons can be made between sources of aggregates, sources of portland cement, and various admixtures. A given material can also be tested and compared with "standard control mixes" for which field service has been established. For these pur-

# 8

# Requirements
# and Recommendations
# for Producing Durable Concrete

GENERAL ACCEPTANCE OF CONCRETE AS ONE OF THE BASIC BUILDING materials makes it mandatory that this confidence be justified by satisfactory performance. Competitive products will replace concrete in many areas where concrete is exposed to freezing and thawing unless the concrete industry can prevent freezing and thawing deterioration. There are two basic approaches in prevention of deterioration of concrete due to freezing and thawing: (1) Produce concrete which is inherently durable and which will withstand freezing and thawing indefinitely; and (2) Provide protection for concrete structures which are exposed to freezing and thawing.

## PRODUCTION OF DURABLE CONCRETE

Methods for producing durable concrete include the following:

1. Produce high quality portland cement paste by limiting the amount of water in proportion to cement used in the concrete mix.

2. Use only high quality aggregates which have satisfactory performance records.
3. Use the proper amount of air-entraining agent to produce an air-bubble spacing which will relieve hydraulic pressures and reduce the growth of capillary ice.
4. Prevent rapid drying of pavement surfaces, and never
give a final finish to a concrete slab until bleeding has
stopped.

## Water-Cement Ratio and Air Entrainment

Portland cement pastes of low water-cement ratio are
more resistant to the buildup of hydraulic pressures and the
growth of capillary ice because there are fewer capillaries in
the paste. It has been estimated by Woods[25] that if a water-
cement ratio below 0.42 by weight could be used in concrete,
the small number of capillaries in the paste would be invul-
nerable to freezing and thawing. The Bureau of Reclamation
experiments have produced durable concrete with a water-
cement ratio of 0.35.[9] Such low water-cement ratios are generally not practical in concrete construction. Water-cement
ratios can be lowered where low slumps can be used, and can
be further lowered by use of chemical admixtures.

Powers[20] shows, on the other hand, that even where there
are fewer capillaries in the portland cement paste, these capillaries must be protected by air voids should they become filled
with water. If this protection is not provided, the development
of hydraulic pressures from the existing capillaries, although
not as extensive as in paste of higher water-cement ratios,
would be sufficient to cause deterioration. Powers also indicates that any paste will be protected, to some extent, by the
proper amount of air entrainment. Approximately the same
durability was found with pastes of different water-cement ratios with proper air entrainment. Tests by Merrill[26] corroborate
these results and show that in ordinary concrete lower durability may be expected in any concrete which contains less
than 2½ percent entrained air (Figure 8.1). The points plotted
in Figure 8.1 came from concrete mixes of low and high water-
cement ratios, containing 4, 5, and 6 bags of cement. Tests
by Klieger[27] show similar results (Figure 8.2), and indicate a

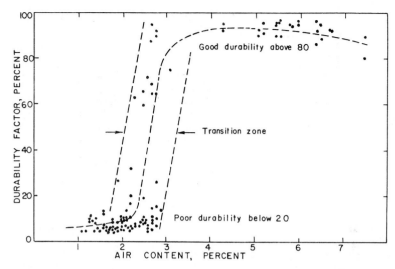

Figure 8.1—Durability of concrete containing various aggregates, with varying cement content, water-cement ratios and air contents (after Cordon and Merrill, Reference 26).

definite transition zone of about 2 to 4 percent air for durable and nondurable concrete even with differences in cement content from 4 bags to 7 bags per cu yd.

The importance of air entrainment in producing durable concrete does not refute the theory that more durable concrete is produced with lower water-cement ratios. Tests by the U. S. Bureau of Reclamation* show that high quality concrete (low water-cement ratio paste) was correspondingly more durable with air entrainment than low quality concrete (high water-cement ratio paste) which was also protected with air entrainment.[28]

Relative improvement of durability due to air entrainment is far greater, however, than improved durability experienced when the water-cement ratio is decreased. For example, the decrease in water-cement ratio from approximately 6½ gal. per bag of cement to 5 gal. per bag may increase freezing and thawing resistance 100 percent (produce concrete which is twice as durable). The addition of approximately 5 percent

---

* See Figure 15 of Reference 28.

air to the same concrete, however, may increase the resistance to freezing and thawing ten times (or 1000 percent).

## Water Content

The water content of a concrete mix may indirectly control the water-cement ratio, since the water-cement ratio may be decreased by increasing the cement content or by decreasing the water content. Additional water in excess of the amount required for hydration of the paste leaves capillary cavities within the hardened paste. The use of a minimum amount of water in fresh concrete is, therefore, highly desirable. Low water contents also increase the strength and decrease the shrinkage.

Shrinkage in concrete occurs as water is drawn from the gel pores of the cement paste and is, therefore, a function of the quantity of paste in the concrete. It is more desirable, therefore, to decrease the water content and paste content in producing a low water-cement ratio, rather than increasing the cement content. The water content of a concrete mix can be decreased by placing concrete at the lowest practical slump and by properly proportioning aggregates. Proper grading of aggregates reduces the voids among the aggregate particles and reduces the surface area of the aggregate, both of which influence the water requirement.

## Water-Reducing Admixtures

The water content of a concrete mix may also be reduced by the use of chemical admixtures commonly referred to as water-reducing admixtures. The admixture anions are absorbed by the cement particles endowing them with negative electrical charges. Individual cement particles in the cement paste will repel rather than attract each other. During mechanical mixing of concrete, the cement flocs are broken up and the cement particles are dispersed releasing about 10 percent of the mixing water which is normally entrapped by the flocs. This permits a reduction of about 5 to 15 percent of the average water content. Dispersing of cement flocs also densifies the cement paste by reducing the amount of uncombined water within the paste. This may result in fewer capillary voids in the gel even at the same water-cement ratio.

Retarding agents may also influence the durability of concrete by reducing the number of capillary voids in the cement paste. The heavier ingredients of fresh concrete tend to settle in the plastic mix. Water, being the lightest ingredient, rises to the surface. This process is known as bleeding or water gain. If the time of set is retarded, more of the mixing water bleeds to the surface thus reducing the number of voids caused by excess, uncombined water. As water rises to the surface, small capillary passages may develop, however, and excessive bleeding may provide easy access for surface

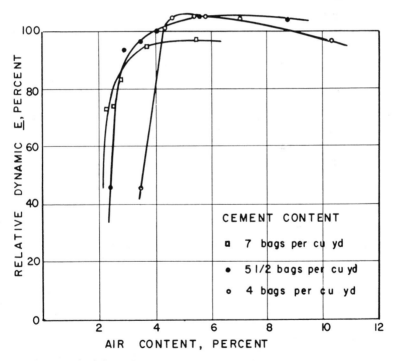

Figure 8.2—Durability of concrete containing 1½-in. maximum aggregate after 300 cycles of freezing and thawing (based on work of Klieger reported in Reference 27).

water. Wallace and Ore[29] reported 39 percent greater resistance to freezing and thawing with the use of water-reducing admixtures.

## Concrete Aggregates

It is not possible to adjust the ingredients of a concrete mix to produce durable concrete if the aggregate particles expand, fracture, or force excessive amounts of freezable water into the surrounding paste as freezing progresses. The only apparent solution to the problem of nondurable aggregates is to limit the quantity of susceptible materials which may be used.

Sweet and Woods[30] found that certain aggregates caused deterioration of concrete regardless of construction practices or the amount of cement used. They also suggested that standard aggregate tests are not adequate in many cases to detect such materials. The failure of standard tests to detect all materials which are not resistant to frost may be attributed to:

(a) Failure to consider the degree of saturation of the material at the time it is incorporated in the concrete.
(b) Failure to duplicate the action of the mortar surrounding the aggregate particles.

This suggests that *performance tests* for aggregates used in standard concrete mixes and exposed to freezing and thawing may be more realistic than tests of the properties of the aggregates themselves.

Lewis and Dolch[16] recognized the correlation of absorption, degree of saturation, and durability and found that the lack of durability of aggregate in freezing and thawing depends primarily on its ability to become and stay highly saturated under given moisture conditions.

A limit on aggregate absorption may eliminate certain aggregates which have poor durability in freezing and thawing although they may pass standard tests for sodium sulfate soundness and abrasion resistance. Indiscriminate use of this criterion may also exclude some durable aggregates with suitable pore structure.

In a study of chert and shale gravel in concrete, Schuster and McLaughlin[31] concluded:

> Despite significant differences in the mineralogies, no difference was noted in the freeze-thaw durabilities of various chert samples. For all the cherts, significant deep-seated and surface deterioration occurred only in beams containing six to ten percent of material having a bulk specific gravity (saturated surface-dry basis) of less than 2.45.

> Although the basic properties of the shales varied even more widely than those of cherts, none of the shales caused deep-seated failure of the concrete. However, the most porous shales caused "popout" damage, which was especially severe at the six and ten percent absorption levels.

The above conclusions indicate that, as far as the cherts used in the tests were concerned, the elimination of the lighter materials (specific gravity below 2.45) would produce a durable aggregate. In the case of shale only, the most porous shale caused popouts. These results suggest the possibility of beneficiation of the chert sources and a method of rejecting shale aggregates by limiting the absorption to an acceptable maximum.

## Beneficiation of Aggregates

Commercial methods are used to produce acceptable aggregates from deposits which contain inferior materials. Methods of upgrading the quality of commercial aggregates include heavy media separation, use of the cage mill, elastic fractionation, and jigging.

*Heavy media separation* floats off the lightweight aggregates in a heavy liquid consisting of water containing finely ground, heavy, high density materials such as magnetite and ferrosilicon.

The *cage mill* consists of a single wheel, about 3 ft in diameter, rotating on a horizontal shaft and enclosed within a strong steel enclosure. Round steel bars about 4½ inches in diameter are mounted on the periphery of the wheel. Gravel is fed into the center of the spinning cage and the weak aggregate particles are broken up when struck with the bars or when thrown against the housing.

*Elastic fractionation* is based on the assumption that good and inferior quality aggregate particles may be separated by allowing them to fall on an inclined plate of hardened steel. The hard, elastic particles will rebound a considerable distance. The soft, friable particles may ricochet only a short distance or may actually disintegrate.

*Jigging* provides gravity separation of gravel by "hindered settling" in water which is subjected to continuous upward pulsation. The lighter material will tend toward the top and the heavier aggregates will sink to the bottom. Separation of the heavy and light aggregates is made by splitting the suspension at the proper height.

Heavy media separation was used successfully by the U. S. Bureau of Reclamation in the construction of Glen Canyon Dam.[9] The undesirable material in this case was a light chert of low specific gravity.

The experience in Michigan with aggregate beneficiation as reported by Legg and McLaughlin[32] is typical of a problem in many parts of the country as high quality aggregate sources are becoming depleted.

> Establishment of the several beneficiation plants is bound to have a salutary influence on over-all concrete quality in the area. Despite greatly increased production of aggregates in recent years, relaxation of quality standards has been unnecessary. Beneficiation has enabled some gravel producers not only to survive competition, but to be able to furnish premium aggregates complying with rigid specifications for architectural concrete where severe exposure conditions are anticipated.

## Pozzolans and Mineral Admixtures

The use of pozzolans in concrete reduces its porosity and permeability.[28] The finely ground reactive silica combines chemically with the hydration product $Ca(OH)_2$. This produces a silica gel which occupies pore space initially occupied by the soluble alkalies and water. One could assume that the use of pozzolans tends to increase freezing and thawing resistance by reducing capillary voids in much the same manner as an increase in portland cement. Tests made with commercial pozzolans[33, 34, 35] indicate that pozzolans do not have significant influence in increasing freezing and thawing durability, and may tend to decrease durability in some instances.

It is generally known that the addition of finely divided mineral filler material decreases permeability of concrete. The reduction in permeability is accomplished because of the increased surface area and reduction in the size of capillary voids. This reduction in the size of capillaries decreases the rate of flow of water under pressure, but does not preclude the saturation of concrete if exposed to moisture for a sufficient length of time. Moreover, the movement of water from the capillaries is also retarded and greater hydraulic pressure is developed as the concrete freezes.

## Air Entrainment

The use of air entrainment in concrete is discussed in Chapter 6. With complete disregard of the known beneficial effects of air entrainment, many specification writers still leave its use to the discretion of the contractor or the finisher. It is axiomatic that *exposed concrete which may become saturated should never be placed in freezing climates without the protection of entrained air.*

## Surface Drying

The compacting mechanisms which occur in the drying surface of fresh concrete and in finishing, before bleeding has stopped, should be prevented for pavements which will be exposed to freezing temperatures. Recommended procedures for preventing rapid evaporation from concrete surfaces are listed by ACI Committee 305, Hot Weather Concreting (formerly Committee 605); they stress protection against high temperatures of ingredients and forms and exposure to wind and sun. A recent development reported by Cordon and Thorpe[36] employs the use of a monomolecular film which is sprayed on fresh concrete and reduces evaporation due to wind about 80 percent and evaporation due to sun about 40 percent. The moisture film can be maintained until bleeding has stopped.

## PROTECTION OF CONCRETE STRUCTURES

Major emphasis in the laboratory and field has been placed on producing durable concrete. However, only saturated concretes are damaged by freezing and thawing action; if the surface of dry concrete could be effectively sealed to the ingress of water, damage to the concrete by freezing and thawing mechanisms could not occur.

An investigation has recently been completed by the Texas Transportation Institute and the Texas Highway Department[37] where 19 waterproofing compounds were tested for reducing water absorption and increasing freezing and thawing resistance. It was found that it is possible to reduce the absorption from 1.13 percent to 0.34 percent with a significant increase in the number of cycles of freezing and thawing. The following excerpts are from the conclusions of this report:

It was found that three boiled linseed oil treatments and a one-component epoxy chlorinated rubber formulation were the top four ranking treatments based on minimum percentage of water absorption and maximum number of freeze-thaw cycles.

The costs of the linseed oil treatments are considerably lower than any other of the seven listed (materials costs as low as 0.33 cents per sq ft). The linseed oil formulations used in the Texas investigations included cold and hot application and 50:50 combination with kerosene or mineral thinners.

A recent bulletin from the U.S. Department of Agriculture (February 1964) indicates success in the use of linseed oil emulsion. Linseed oil emulsions show promise in U.S. Department of Agriculture studies for safe, low-cost use in curing concrete and protecting it against damage by freezing and thawing.

When emulsions of the new compositions are applied to concrete, the linseed oil forms a film that reduces the movement of water into or out of the concrete. Reducing movement of water from fresh concrete aids strength development. Movement of water into cured concrete and freezing and thawing cause pitting and scaling. This damage increases when salt is used to remove ice and snow.

Curing evaluations, carried out by C. H. Best and C. H. Scholer at Kansas State University as one part of the research contract, indicate that commercial development of linseed-oil curing agents is feasible. Such commercialization could result in a large new market for linseed oil.

Evaluation of the experimental compositions to protect concrete against scaling, another part of the contract, is still under way.

Experience shows that linseed oil has value as an anti-scaling agent. Solutions of this oil and flammable solvents are sprayed on highways, streets, and bridges to reduce damage caused by salt.

The Bureau of Reclamation *Concrete Manual*[28] recommends a linseed oil-paint treatment as a protective measure for concrete.

## RECOMMENDATIONS FOR FREEZING AND THAWING DURABILITY FOR CONCRETE

The several mechanisms responsible for freezing and thawing deterioration of concrete make the prevention and control of such deterioration varied and complex. However, it is believed that simple precautions at the proper time could have prevented many freezing and thawing failures. The following "do" and "don't" recommendations have been compiled for improved concrete construction and control methods. Perhaps only one or two of these items would apply to freezing and thawing deterioration under any given set of conditions, but all are considered good, workable practices.

1. *Entrain 4 to 6 percent air in all exposed concrete that may be saturated in freezing weather.*

Entrained air relieves hydraulic pressures in freezing gel structure and competes with capillary ice for available moisture, thus limiting two of the most important deterioration mechanisms.

2. *Avoid concrete aggregates having high absorption.*

It may be ascertained that the pore structure of the aggregate particles is such that the aggregate itself is not susceptible to freezing and thawing damage. It should also be demonstrated by test, however, that the aggregates do not contribute to freezing and thawing deterioration when used in concrete subjected to field exposure conditions.

3. *Use the minimum amount of mixing water possible, commensurate with good construction practices.*

Excess water in fresh concrete results in an increase in capillary voids in the hardened paste. Capillary voids are the starting point for several deterioration mechanisms.

Excess water also increases the amount of bleeding water. This could be important in the development of a surface structure which is susceptible to scaling.

4. *Avoid saturation of exposed concrete in freezing weather.*

Most freezing and thawing deterioration mechanisms will not take place unless sufficient moisture is available to produce critical saturation.

5. *Be sure the hydration of portland cement is well advanced before concrete is subjected to freezing and thawing.*

Concrete which contains unhydrated portland cement is weak and will contain more capillary voids than the same concrete when hydration is complete. Accretion of water from unhydrated paste in cold weather may cause crazing.

6. *Prevent rapid drying of the surface of exposed concrete before the bleeding is complete.*

The drying surface of fresh concrete is compacted by capillary forces. This compacted surface may trap bleeding water below the surface, producing a weak, porous zone im-

Figure 8.3—Sidewalk with continuous severe scaling on the left side, and no scaling on the right side. Snow from the parking lot was piled on the left side of the walk, but not on the right.

mediately beneath the surface layer, thus creating a surface "scaling structure."

7. *Do not finish the surface of exposed concrete until bleed water has disappeared.*

Finishing operations densify the surface of concrete, preventing the escape of subsequent bleeding water, and again a "scaling structure" is formed. After bleeding has stopped, floating and compaction have a beneficial effect.[38]

8. *Avoid the use of salts for ice or snow removal.*

Salt will melt snow and ice, thus replenishing the moisture supply available to capillary voids. Salts also lower the temperature of concrete beneath the surface and thereby create additional freezing potential.

Concentration of salt in capillary voids increases scaling tendencies due to osmotic pressure.

9. *After curing, allow exposed concrete to dry as much as possible; then seal the surface.*

A sealing compound, thinned to allow maximum penetration, will fill surface capillaries, thus reducing absorption of water. Unless additional water channels to areas below the surface develop due to cracking or crazing, the concrete will resist saturation and consequent freezing and thawing deterioration mechanisms. If crazing or cracking occurs, additional applications should be made.

10. *Provide adequate drainage for all exposed concrete surfaces.*

It is obviously impossible to prevent rain or snow from falling on concrete pavements and structures. It may be possible to provide slopes which will permit moisture to drain from the surface and reduce saturation.

Laboratory investigations[15] indicate that the mechanism or combination of mechanisms which cause freezing and thawing deterioration may be very discriminating. The new sidewalk in Figure 8.3 shows severe scaling on one side and none on the other. The only known difference between the two sides was that snow from the adjacent parking lot was piled on the left side and not on the right.

# References

1.  Joint Committee on Standard Specifications for Concrete and Reinforced Concrete, "Recommended Practice and Standard Specifications for Concrete and Reinforced Concrete," (prepared by affiliated committees of ACI, AIA, AREA, ASCE, ASTM and PCA) American Concrete Institute, Detroit, 1940, 271 pp.

2.  Swayze, M. A., "More Durable Concrete with Treated Cement," *Engineering News-Record,* V. 126, 1941, pp. 946–949.

3.  "Concretes Containing Air-Entraining Agents—A Symposium," ACI JOURNAL, *Proceedings* V. 40, No. 6, June 1944, pp. 509–569.

Jackson, F. H., "An Introduction and Questions to Which Answers Are Sought," pp. 509–515.

Kennedy, H. L., "The Function of Entrained Air in Portland Cement," pp. 515–517.

Meissner, Harmon S., "Laboratory Freezing and Thawing Tests on Concretes Containing Various Air-Entraining Agents," pp. 517–522.

Swayze, Myron A., "Air Entrainment Calls for Changes in Mix Design and Mixing Practice," pp. 522–524.

MacPherson, Donald R., "Methods of Entraining Air in Concrete," pp. 524–529.

Lindsay, George L., "Manufacture and Use of Air-Entraining Portland Cement," pp. 529–536.

Thomson, Harry F., "Aeration, Offering Improved Concreting, Should Be Used with Caution," pp. 536–538.

Burmeister, R. A., "Milwaukee's Experience with Air-Entraining Cements," p. 539–547.

Walker, Stanton, "Air-Entraining Cements in Ready-Mixed Concrete Industry," pp. 547–551.

Davis, Raymond E., "Entrained Air Beneficial in Freezing and Thawing Tests," p. 522.

Larson, G. H., "Field Experiences with Concrete Containing Air-Entraining Cement," pp. 552–554.

Chubb, J. H., "Laboratory and Field Experiences," pp. 554–557.

Sherrod, R. T., "Effect of Air-Entraining Agents on Pumped Concrete," pp. 558–560.

Barbee, J. F., "Air-Entraining Agents in Ohio Highways," pp. 560–563.

Reagel, F. V., "Air-Entraining Agents Not a Cure-All," pp. 563–567.

Jackson, F. H., "Concluding Summary," pp. 567–569.

4. "Entrained Air in Concrete—A Symposium," ACI JOURNAL, *Proceedings* V. 42, No. 6, June 1946, pp. 601–696. Contributions to the symposium are listed below:

Cordon, W. A., "Entrained Air, A Factor in the Design of Concrete Mixes," pp. 605–620.

Andrews, L. E., "Recent Experiences with Air-Entraining Portland Cement Concrete in the Northeastern States," pp. 621–624.

Foster, Alexander, Jr., "Experiences with Air-Entraining Cement in Central-Mixed Concrete," pp. 625–628.

Walker, Stanton, and Bloem, Delmar L., "Studies of Concrete Containing Entrained Air," pp. 629–639.

Kennedy. H. L., "Homogeneity of Air-Entraining Concrete," pp. 641–644.

Scripture, E. W., Jr., "Methods of Entraining Air in Concrete," pp. 645–648.

Goldbeck, A. T., "Effect of Air Entrainment on Stone Sand Concrete," pp. 649–654.

Klein, W. H., and Walker, Stanton, "A Method of Direct Measurement of Entrained Air in Concrete," pp. 657–668.

Kaufman, R. R., "Automatic Dispensing Equipment for Air-Entraining Agents," pp. 669–672.

Brickett, E. M., "Mechanical Dispensing Devices for Air-Entraining Agents," pp. 673–676.

Benham, S. W., "A Simple Accurate Method for Determining Entrained Air in Fresh Concrete," pp. 677–680.

Kellermann, W. F., "Effect of Use of Blended Cements and Vinsol Resin-Treated Cements on Durability of Concrete," pp. 681–687.

Herman, W. H., "Air-Entraining Concrete—Pennsylvania Department of Highways," pp. 689–694.
Wait, B. H., "Portable-Rosendale Cement Blends Give High Frost Resistance," pp. 697–699.

5. Cook, H. K., "Experimental Exposure of Concrete to Natural Weathering in Marine Locations," *Proceedings*, ASTM, V. 52, 1952, pp. 1169–1180.
6. Verbeck, G. J., and Klieger, Paul, "Studies of Salt Scaling of Concrete," *Bulletin* 150, Highway Research Board, 1957.
7. Kleiger, Paul, "Effect of Atmospheric Conditions During the Bleeding Period and Time of Finishing on the Scale Resistance of Concrete," ACI JOURNAL, *Proceedings* V. 52, No. 3, Nov. 1955, pp. 309–326.
8. "Resistance of Materials to Frost Action," *Tonindustrie-Zeitung*, V. 52, No. 33, 1928, p. 658.
9. Troxell, E. G., and Davis, H. E., *Concrete*, McGraw-Hill, New York, 1956, 204 pp.
10. Brunauer, Stephen, "Tobermorite Gel—The Heart of Concrete," *American Scientist*, Mar. 1962.
11. Copeland, L. E., and Schulz, Edith G., "Electron Optical Investigation of the Hydration Products of Calcium Silicates and Portland Cement," *Journal*, PCA Research and Development Laboratories, Jan. 1962.
12. Brunauer, Stephen, and Copeland, L. E., "The Chemistry of Concrete," *Scientific-American*, 1964.
13. Powers, T. C., and Helmuth, R. A., "Theory of Volume Changes in Hardened Portland-Cement Paste During Freezing," *Proceedings*, Highway Research Board, V. 32, 1953, pp. 285–297.
14. Powers, T. C., "The Bleeding of Portland Cement Paste, Mortar and Concrete," *Bulletin* No. 2, PCA Research Laboratory, 1939.
15. Walburger, Russell, "Scaling of Concrete Surfaces," *Bulletin*, Engineering Experiment Station, Utah State University, 1966 (a graduate thesis).
16. "Significance of Tests and Properties of Concrete and Concrete Aggregates," ASTM *STP* 169, 1956, including the following contributions:

Lewis, D. W., and Dolch, W. L., "Porosity and Absorption."
Powers, T. C., "Resistance to Weathering—Freezing and Thawing."
Verbeck, George, "Pore Structure."
Scholer, C. H., "Resistance to Weathering—General Aspects."

17. Verbeck, George, and Landgren, Robert, "Influence of Physical Characteristics of Aggregates on Frost Resistance of Concrete," *Proceedings*, ASTM, V. 60, 1960, pp. 1063–1079.

18. Blanks, R. F., and Cordon, W. A., "Practices, Experiences and Tests with Air-Entraining Agents in Making Durable Concrete," ACI JOURNAL, *Proceedings* V. 45, 1949, pp. 469–487.

19. "Use of Air-Entraining Concrete in Pavements and Bridges," *Current Road Problems* (a Highway Research Board publication), No. 13-R, May 1950, 74 pp.

20. Powers, T. C., "The Air Requirement of Frost-Resistant Concrete," *Proceedings*, Highway Research Board, V. 29, 1949, pp. 184–211.

21. Mielenz, R. C.; Backstrom, J. E.; Burrows, R. W.; Wolkodoff, V. E.; and Flack, H. L., "Origin, Evolution, and Effects of the Air Void System in Concrete," ACI JOURNAL, *Proceedings* V. 55, No. 1–3, July-Sept. 1958, pp. 95–122, 261–272, and 359–376.

22. Powers, T. C., "Void Spacing as a Basis for Producing Air-Entrained Concrete," ACI JOURNAL, *Proceedings* V. 50, No. 9, May 1954, pp. 741–760.

23. Cordon, W. A., and Brewer, H. W., "Analysis of Methods of Measuring Entrained Air in Concrete," *Proceedings*, ASTM, V. 47, 1947, p. 893.

24. Tremper, Bailey, and Spellman, D. L., "Tests for Freeze-Thaw Durability of Concrete Aggregates," *Bulletin* 305, Highway Research Board, 1961, pp. 28–50.

25. Woods, Hubert, "Observations on the Resistance of Concrete to Freezing and Thawing," ACI JOURNAL, *Proceedings* V. 51, No. 4, Dec. 1954, pp. 345–352.

26. Cordon, W. A., and Merrill, Derwin, "Requirements for Freezing and Thawing Durability for Concrete," *Proceedings*, ASTM, V. 63, 1963, pp. 1026–1036.

27. Klieger, Paul, "The Effect of Entrained Air on Strength and Durability of Concrete Made with Various Sizes of Aggregates," Highway Research Board, *Bulletin* 128, 1956, pp. 1–19.

28. *Concrete Manual*, U.S. Bureau of Reclamation, Denver, 7th edition, 1963.

29. Wallace, G. B., and Ore, E. L., "Structural and Lean Mass Concrete as Affected by Water-Reducing, Set-Retarding Agents," ASTM *STP* 266, 1959, p. 38.

30. Sweet, H. S., and Woods, K. B., "A Study of Chert as a Deleterious Constituent in Aggregates," Purdue University, *Engineering Bulletin*, V. 26, No. 5 (Research Series No. 86), Sept. 1942.

31. Schuster, R. L., and McLaughlin, J. F., "A Study of Chert and Shale Gravel in Concrete," *Bulletin* 305, Highway Research Board, 1961, pp. 51–75.

32. Legg, F. E., Jr., "Freeze-Thaw Durability of Michigan Concrete Coarse Aggregates," *Bulletin* 143, Highway Research Board, 1956, pp. 1–13.

33. Blanks, R. F.; Meissner, H. S.; and Cordon, W. A., "The Properties of Mass Concrete Made With Combinations of Portland and Pozzolan Cement," International Commission on Large Dams, India, 1951.

34. Washa, G. W., and Withey, N. H., "Strength and Durability of Concrete Containing Chicago Fly Ash," ACI JOURNAL, *Proceedings* V. 49, No. 8, Apr. 1953, pp. 701–712.

35. Greib, W. E.; Werner, G.; and Woolf, D. O., "Resistance of Concrete Surfaces to Scaling by De-Icing Agents," *Public Roads* V. 32, 1962.

36. Cordon, W. A., and Thorpe, J. D., "Control of Rapid Drying of Fresh Concrete by Evaporation Control," ACI JOURNAL, *Proceedings* V. 62, No. 8, Aug. 1965, pp. 977–986.

37. Furr, H. L., "Moisture Protection for Concrete," Texas Transportation Institute, Sept. 1963.

38. Swayze, M. A., "Finishing and Curing: A Key to Durability of Concrete Surfaces," ACI JOURNAL, *Proceedings* V. 47, No. 4, Dec. 1950, pp. 317–332.

# Selected Bibliography

1. Vicat, L. J., "Treatise on Calcareous Mortars and Cements" (translated from the French by J. T. Smith), J. Weale, London, 1837.

2. "Effect of Frost on Concrete," *Report*, U.S. Army, Chief of Engineers, 1905, p. 1987.

3. McDaniel, A. B., "Freezing and Thawing—Effect on Concrete," (abstract) *Concrete*, V. 18, No. 8, Sept. 1918, p. 84.

4. Washburn, E. W., "Porosity and the Mechanism of Absorption," *Journal*, American Ceramic Society, V. 4, 1921, pp. 916–922.

5. Abrams, D. A., "Influence of Aggregates on the Durability of Concrete," *Proceedings*, ASTM, V. 23, Part 2, 1923, pp. 172–174.

6. Loughlin, G. F., "Qualifications of Different Kinds of Natural Stone for Concrete Aggregate," ACI *Proceedings* V. 23, 1927, pp. 319–351; discussion, pp. 352–354.

7. Woolf, D. O., "Relation Between Absorption and Soundness Test of Sedimentary Rock," *Public Roads*, V. 8, No. 10, 1927, pp. 225–227; *Rock Products*, V. 31, No. 1, Jan. 7, 1928, pp. 39–40.

8. Petry, W., "Deterioration of Concrete," *Tonindustrie-Zeitung*, V. 52, 1928, pp. 398–399; *Building Science Abstracts*, V. 1, June 1928, p. 168.

9. Anderegg, F. O., "The Mechanism of Corrosion of Portland Cement Concrete with Special Reference to Role of Crystal Pressure," ACI *Proceedings* V. 25, 1929, pp. 332–343.

10. Hogentogler, C. A., and Willis, E. A., "Discussion on the Durability of Concrete: The Phenomenon of Shrinkage and Its Effects upon the Integrity and Durability of Concrete Pavements," *Proceedings,* Highway Research Board, V. 10, 1930, pp. 164–205.

11. Jackson, F. H., "Relationship between Durability of Concrete and Durability of Aggregates," *Proceedings,* Highway Research Board, V. 10, 1930, pp. 103–113; discussion, pp. 113–131; *Crushed Stone Journal,* V. 6, No. 12, Dec. 1930, pp. 5–9.

12. Lang, F. C., and Hughes, C. A., "Discussion on Relation Between Durability of Concrete and Durability of Aggregates," *Proceedings,* Highway Research Board, V. 10, 1930, pp. 113–131.

13. Scholer, C. H., "Durability of Concrete," *Proceedings,* Highway Research Board, V. 10, 1930, pp. 132–163.

14. Walker, Stanton, "Effects of Characteristics of Coarse Aggregates on Quality of Concrete," *Bulletin* No. 5, National Sand and Gravel Association, 1930.

15. Emmons, W. J., "The Effect of Soft Particles of Coarse Aggregate on the Strength and Durability of Concrete," *Circular* No. 6, National Sand and Gravel Association, 1931.

16. Gonnerman, H. F., "Researches on the Durability of Concrete," *Crushed Stone Journal,* V. 7, No. 5, May 1931, pp. 15–18; *Canadian Engineer,* V. 61, No. 7, Aug. 18, 1931, pp. 19–20.

17. Withey, M. C., "Some Long-Time Tests of Concrete," ACI JOURNAL, *Proceedings* V. 27, No. 6, Feb. 1931, pp. 547–548.

18. Jackson, F. H., and Werner, George, "The Resistance of Concrete to Frost Action," *Public Roads,* V. 13, No. 2, 1932, pp. 32–38.

19. Scholer, C. H., and Stoddard, A. E., "Proposed Method of Testing Concrete and Concrete Aggregates by Freezing and Thawing," *Proceedings,* ASTM, V. 32, Part 1, 1932, pp. 364–366.

20. Hanson, L. O., "Weathering Tests of Concrete," *Proceedings,* Highway Research Board, V. 13, Part 1, 1933, pp. 303–326.

21. Lyse, Inge, and Holme, J. M., "Durability Studies of Concrete and Aggregates," ACI JOURNAL, *Proceedings* V. 30, No. 2, Nov.-Dec. 1933, pp. 121–128.

22. Parsons, D. A., "Clay in Concrete," *Journal of Research* (U.S. Bureau of Standards), V. 10, Feb. 1933, pp. 257–273.

23. Walker, Stanton, "Soundness of Aggregates," ASTM *Bulletin,* No. 73, Mar. 1935, p. 75.

24. Griffith, J. H., "Thermal Expansion of Typical American Rocks," *Bulletin* No. 128, Iowa Engineering Experiment Station, Oct., 1936.

25. Scholer, C. H., "Studying the Durability of Concrete," ACI JOURNAL, *Proceedings* V. 32, No. 6, May-June 1936, pp. 593–607.

26. Paul, Ira, "Chloride-Salt Resistant Concrete in Pavements," *Proceedings*, 14th Annual Convention, Association of State Highway Officials of North Atlantic States, 1938, pp. 144–167.

27. Campbell, Louis, and Cantrill, Curtis, "Selection of Aggregates for Concrete Pavement Based on Service Records," *Proceedings*, ASTM, V. 39, 1939, pp. 937–945; discussion, pp. 946–949.

28. Hornibrook, F. B., "Sonic Method for Studying Effect of Freezing and Thawing on Concrete," ASTM *Bulletin* No. 101, Dec. 1939, pp. 5–9. *Technical News Bulletin* (U.S. Bureau of Standards), No. 272, 1939, p. 127.

29. Lawton, E. C., "Durability of Concrete Pavements—Experiences in New York State," ACI JOURNAL, *Proceedings* V. 35, No. 6, June 1939, pp. 561–578.

30. Pickett, G., "The Effect of Biot's Modulus on Transient Thermal Stresses in Concrete Cylinders," *Proceedings*, ASTM, V. 39, 1939, pp. 913–918.

31. Withey, M. O., "Factors Affecting the Resistance to Freezing and Thawing of Vibrated Concrete Made of Crushed Dolomite," ACI JOURNAL, *Proceedings* V. 35, No. 6, June 1939, pp. 553–560.

32. Sweet, H. S., "Chert as a Deleterious Constituent in Indiana Aggregates," *Proceedings*, Highway Research Board, V. 20, 1940, pp. 599–620.

33. Wuerpel, C. E., "Detecting Unsound Chert in Aggregates," *Engineering News-Record*, V. 124, 1940, pp. 652–654.

34. Anderson, A. A., "Experimental Test Data in Connection with the Development of Chloride-Resisting Concrete by the Use of Treated Portland Cements and Blends with Natural Cement," *Proceedings*, 17th Annual Convention, Association of Highway Officials of North Atlantic States, 1941, pp. 67–89; *Explosives Engineer*, V. 20, Jan. 1942, pp. 10–14, 26–30.

35. Hughes, C. A., and Andersen, K. A., "The Effect of Fine Aggregate on the Durability of Mortars," *Proceedings*, ASTM, V. 41, 1941, pp. 987–1002.

36. Reagel, F. V., and Gotham, Don E., "Field Observations on Effects of Joints on Cracking and Other Deterioration in Concrete Pavements," *Proceedings*, Highway Research Board, V. 21, 1941, pp. 179–205.

37. Hansen, W. C., "Influence of Sands, Cements and Manipulation upon the Resistance of Concrete to Freezing and Thawing," ACI JOURNAL, *Proceedings* V. 39, Nov. 1942, pp. 105–123.

38. Munger, H. H., "The Influence of the Durability of Aggregate Upon the Durability of the Resulting Concrete," *Proceedings*, ASTM, V. 42, 1942, pp. 787–803; discussion, pp. 804–807.

39. Kennedy, H. L., "The Function of Entrained Air in Concrete," ACI JOURNAL, *Proceedings* V. 39, No. 6, June 1943, pp. 529–542.

40. Walker, Stanton, "Discussion on Freezing and Thawing of Concrete," *Proceedings*, ASTM, V. 43, 1943, pp. 996–999.

41. Bartell, F. F., "Effects of Aggregate Characteristics on Durability of Concrete," (Abstract) ACI JOURNAL, *Proceedings* V. 40, No. 1, Sept. 1943, p. 85.

42. Collins, A. R., "The Destruction of Concrete by Frost," *Journal*, Institution of Civil Engineers (London), V. 23, 1944, pp. 29–48.

43. Gonnerman, H. F., "Tests of Concretes Containing Air-Entraining Portland Cements or Air-Entraining Materials Added to Batch at Mixer," ACI JOURNAL, *Proceedings* V. 40, No. 6, June 1944, pp. 477–507.

44. Johnson, W. H., and Parsons, W. H., "Thermal Expansion of Concrete Aggregate Materials," *Journal of Research* (U.S. Bureau of Standards), V. 32, 1944, pp. 101–126.

45. Parsons, W. H., and Johnson, W. H., "Factors Affecting the Thermal Expansion of Concrete Aggregate Materials," ACI JOURNAL, *Proceedings* V. 40, No. 5, Apr. 1944, pp. 457–466.

46. Powers, T. C., "A Working Hypothesis for Further Studies of Frost Resistance of Concrete," ACI JOURNAL, *Proceedings* V. 41, No. 4, Feb. 1945, pp. 245–272.

47. Terzaghi, K., "Stress Conditions for the Failure of Saturated Concrete and Rock," *Proceedings*, ASTM, V. 45, 1945, pp. 777–792.

48. White, L. V., and Peyton, R. L., "Condition of Concrete Pavements in Kansas as Affected by Coarse Aggregate," *Proceedings*, Highway Research Board, V. 25, 1945, pp. 129–146.

49. Wuerpel, C. E., "Field Use of Cement Containing Vinsol Resin," U.S. War Department, Corps of Engineers, Central Concrete Laboratory, Concrete Research, Second Interim Report, Part II, July 1945; ACI JOURNAL, *Proceedings* V. 42, No. 1, Sept. 1945, pp. 49–82.

50. Barbee, J. F., "The Effect of Air Entrainment on the Durability of Concrete Pavement in Ohio," *Crushed Stone Journal*, V. 22, No. 1, Mar. 1946, pp. 28–37.

51. Jackson, F. H., "The Durability of Concrete in Service," ACI JOURNAL, *Proceedings* V. 43, No. 2, Oct. 1946, pp. 165–180.

52. Wuerpel, C. E., "Laboratory Studies of Concrete Containing Air-Entraining Admixtures," ACI JOURNAL, *Proceedings* V. 42, No. 4, Feb. 1946, pp. 305–359.

53. Hornibrook, F. B.; Freiberger, Howard; and Litvin, Albert, "A Study of Durability and Void Characteristics of Concrete Containing Admixtures, Principally of the Air-Entraining Type," *Proceedings*, ASTM, V. 46, 1946, pp. 1320–1332.

54. Klieger, Paul, "Effect of Entrained Air on Concretes Made with So-Called 'Sand-Gravel' Aggregates," ACI JOURNAL, *Proceedings* V. 45, No. 2, Oct. 1948, pp. 149–163.

55. Petersen, P. H., "Burned Shale and Expanded Slag Concretes With and Without Air-Entraining Admixture," ACI JOURNAL, *Proceedings* V. 45, No. 2, Oct. 1948, pp. 164–175.

56. Seaton, S. G., "Study of Causes and Prevention of Staining and Pop-Outs in Cinder Concrete," ACI JOURNAL, *Proceedings* V. 44, No. 5, Jan. 1948, pp. 361–377.

57. Terzaghi, Ruth D., "Concrete Deterioration in a Shipway," ACI JOURNAL, *Proceedings* V. 44, No. 10, June 1948, pp. 977–1005.

58. Powers, T. C., "The Nonevaporable Water Content of Hardened Portland Cement Paste—Its Significance for Concrete Research and Its Method of Determination," ASTM *Bulletin* No. 158, May 1949, p. 68.

59. Tallamy, B. D., "Control of Concrete Pavement Scaling Caused by Chloride Salts," ACI JOURNAL, *Proceedings* V. 45, No. 7, Mar. 1949, pp. 513–520.

60. Whiteside, Thomas M., and Sweet, Harold S., "Effect of Mortar Saturation in Concrete Freezing and Thawing Tests," *Proceedings*, Highway Research Board, V. 30, 1950, pp. 193–204.

61. Woods, K. B., "Aggregates and Their Influence on the Durability of Concrete," *Crushed Stone Journal*, V. 25, No. 1, Mar. 1950, p. 21.

62. Brewer, Harold W., and Burrows, Richard W., "Coarse-Ground Cement Makes More Durable Concrete," ACI JOURNAL, *Proceedings* V. 47, No. 5, Jan. 1951, pp. 353–360.

63. Tremper, Bailey, "Freeze-Thaw Resistance of Concrete as Affected by Alkalies in Cement," *Proceedings*, ASTM, V. 51, 1951, pp. 1097–1107.

64. Walker, Stanton, and Bloem, Delmar L., "Performance of Automatic Freezing-and-Thawing Apparatus for Testing Concrete," *Proceedings*, ASTM, V. 51, 1951, pp. 1120–1135.

65. Porter, C. B.; Gilmore, R. W.; Jackson, F. H.; Tuthill, Lewis H.; and Steele, Byram W., "Durability," ACI JOURNAL, *Proceedings* V. 48, No. 9, May 1952, pp. 725–752.

66. Cook, Herbert K., "Experimental Exposure of Concrete to Natural Weathering in Marine Locations," *Proceedings*, ASTM, V. 52, 1952, pp. 1169–1180.

67. Klieger, Paul, "Effect of Entrained Air on Strength and Durability of Concrete Made with Various Maximum Sizes of Aggregate," *Proceedings*, Highway Research Board, V. 31, 1952, pp. 177–201.

68. Landgren, Robert, and Sweet, H. S., "Investigation of Durability of Wyoming Aggregates," *Proceedings*, Highway Research Board, V. 31, 1952, pp. 202–217.

69. McCoy, W. J., and Helms, S. B., "Performance of Concrete Specimens During 10 Years Exposure to Severe Natural Weathering," *Proceedings*, ASTM, V. 52, 1952, pp. 1182–1196.

70. Scholer, C. H., "Significant Factors Affecting Concrete Durability," *Proceedings*, ASTM, V. 52, 1952, pp. 1145–1156.

71. Scripture, E. W., Jr.; Benedict, S. W.; and Litwinowicz, F. J., "Air Entrainment and Resistance to Freezing and Thawing," ACI JOURNAL, *Proceedings* V. 48, No. 4, Dec. 1951, pp. 297–308.

72. Walker, Stanton; Bloem, D. L.; and Mullen, W. G., "Effects of Temperature Changes on Concrete as Influenced by Aggregates," ACI JOURNAL, *Proceedings* V. 48, No. 8, Apr. 1952, pp. 661–679.

73. Andrews, L. E., "Record of Experimental Air-Entrained Concrete 10 to 14 Years After Construction," *Bulletin* 70, Highway Research Board, 1953, pp. 11–23.

74. Blanks, R. F., "Ten-Year Report on the Long-Time Study of Cement Performance in Concrete," ACI JOURNAL, *Proceedings* V. 49, No. 7, Mar. 1953, pp. 601–616.

75. Higginson, Elmo C., and Kretsinger, D. G., "Prediction of Concrete Durability from Thermal Tests of Aggregate," *Proceedings*, ASTM, V. 53, 1953, pp. 991–1001.

76. Lewis, D. W.; Dolch, W. L.; and Woods, K. B., "Porosity Determinations and the Significance of Pore Characteristics of Aggregates," *Proceedings*, ASTM, V. 53, 1953, pp. 949–962.

77. Pickett, Gerald, "Flow of Moisture in Hardened Portland Cement during Freezing," *Proceedings*, Highway Research Board, V. 32, 1953, pp. 276–284.

78. Hansen, W. C., "Effect of Age of Concrete on Its Resistance to Scaling Caused by Using Calcium Chloride for Ice Removal," ACI JOURNAL, *Proceedings* V. 50, No. 5, Jan. 1954, pp. 341–351.

79. Kennedy, Thomas B., and Mather, Katharine, "Correlation Between Laboratory Accelerated Freezing and Thawing and Weathering at Treat Island, Maine," ACI JOURNAL, *Proceedings* V. 50, No. 2, Oct. 1953, pp. 141–172.

80. Jackson, F. H., "Long-Time Study of Cement Performance in Concrete. Chapter 9—Correlation of the Results of Laboratory Tests with Field Performance Under Natural Freezing and Thawing," ACI JOURNAL, *Proceedings* V. 52, No. 2, Oct. 1955, pp. 159–194.

81. Powers, T. C., "Basic Considerations Pertaining to Freezing-and-Thawing Tests," *Proceedings*, ASTM, V. 55, 1955, pp. 1132–1155.

82. Timms, Albert G., "Resistance of Concrete Surfaces to Scaling Action of Ice-Removal Agents," *Bulletin* 128, Highway Research Board, 1956, pp. 20–50.

83. Walker, R. D., and McLaughlin, J. F., "Effect of Crushed Stone and Heavy Media Separation on the Durability of Concrete Made with Indiana Gravels," *Bulletin* 143, Highway Research Board, 1956, pp. 14–26.

84. Mather, Bryant, "Factors Affecting Durability of Concrete in Coastal Structures," *Technical Memorandum*, No. 96, Beach Erosion Board, June 1957.

85. Klieger, Paul, "Curing Requirements for Scale Resistance of Concrete," *Bulletin* 150, Highway Research Board, 1957.

86. Fears, F. K., "Correlation Between Concrete Durability and Air Void Characteristics," *Bulletin* 196, Highway Research Board, 1958.

87. Jackson, F. H., "Long-Time Study of Cement Performance in Concrete. Chapter 11—Report On the Condition of Three Test Pavements After 15 Years of Service," ACI JOURNAL, *Proceedings* V. 54, No. 12, June 1958, pp. 1017–1032.

88. MacKenzie, I. D., "Heavy Media Processing of Gravels in New Brunswick," ACI JOURNAL, *Proceedings* V. 55, No. 1, July 1958, pp. 133–138.

89. "Cooperative Freezing-and-Thawing Tests of Concrete," *Special Report* No. 47, Highway Research Board, 1959.

90. Tyler, I. L., "Long-Time Study of Cement Performance in Concrete. Chapter 12—Concrete Exposed to Sea Water and Fresh Water," ACI JOURNAL, *Proceedings* V. 56, No. 9, Mar. 1960, pp. 825–836.

91. Miesenhelder, P. D., "Effect of Design and Details On Concrete Deterioration," ACI JOURNAL, *Proceedings* V. 56, No. 7, Jan. 1960, pp. 581–590.

92. Powers, T. C., "The Physical Structure and Engineering Properties of Concrete," *Bulletin* 90, PCA Research and Development Laboratories, July 1958, 22 pp.

# Index

95